CUTTING E

PRE-INTERMEDIATE

WORKBOOK

Longman

peter moor   sarah cunningham

Contents

Introduction

Grammar terms

1 Use the words in the box to describe the words in **bold** below.

~~adjective~~   article (indefinite)   noun (countable)
pronoun   adverb   auxiliary verb
noun (uncountable)   main verb   article (definite)
possessive adjective   modal verb   preposition

a   an **old** woman   a **good** film
a **small** country   *adjective* ....

b   **my** family   **your** name   **his** friends

....

c   **I** like coffee   Where are **you** from?
Do **you** know **her**?   ....

d   **Can** you swim?   It **might** rain tonight.
Could you open the door?   ....

e   Speak **slowly**.   Come back **tomorrow**.
He's **always** late.   ....

f   **Have** you finished?   What time **does** she arrive?
It **will** be cold tomorrow.   ....

g   The film **starts** at 10.   Do you **speak** English?
How do you **spell** it?   ....

h   a **cat**   an **elephant**   **eggs**   ....

i   **the** Internet   **the** time   **the** President

....

j   **money**   **weather**   **homework** ....

k   They're **from** Brazil   **at** 8 o'clock
in the kitchen   ....

l   **a** house   **an** orange   **a** book   ....

2 Look at the song titles below. Find an example of:

a   an auxiliary verb   *do* ....

b   an adjective   ....

c   an indefinite article   ....

d   a countable noun   ....

e   a pronoun   ....

f   an adverb   ....

g   an uncountable noun   ....

h   a main verb   ....

i   a modal verb   ....

j   a possessive adjective   ....

Do you Want to Know a Secret?

Your Kiss Is Sweet

You Can Never Stop My Love

You Might See Me Cry

BOYS WANT TO HAVE FUN

I Will Always Love You

module 1

Question forms

Word order

1 **a)** Michael Aarons, World 100m Champion, is in Rome for an important athletics meeting. Write the journalists' questions by putting the words in the correct order.

1 first time - this - Is - here in Rome - your - ?
   Is this your first time here in Rome ? ....?

   No. I first came here about eight years ago.

2 your family - with - here - Is - you - ?
   ....?

   My wife is here; my children are with their grandparents in the United States.

3 enjoy - wife - Does - athletics - your - ?
   ....?

   She says so, but I think she's really here because she likes shopping!

4 life - you - here in Italy - like - Do - ?
   ....?

   Of course, especially the food and the sunshine!

5 you - about - the Italian champion, Giacomo Zanetti - Are - worried - ?
   ....?

   Giacomo is a great athlete and a good friend ... but I think I can win!

6 you - Do - have - for young athletes - any advice - ?
   ....?

   Sure - train hard, live a healthy life, and you can be a champion too!

b) 📼 Listen to the interview and check your answers.

Question words

2 Use each question word **once** to complete the questions about Parcheesi – the national game of India.

Parcheesi! The National Game of India

| how how long where which who why |
| how many what ~~what sort~~ when |

a *What sort* of game is Parcheesi?

It's a board game - like chess or backgammon.

b .... country does it come from originally?

India.

c .... do people play it now?

All over the world – it's very popular in the USA.

d .... does 'Parcheesi' mean?

It comes from 'pacis', which means 25.

e .... did people start playing it?

Hundreds of years ago: but it only came to Europe in the 19th century.

f .... invented it?

Nobody knows!

g .... people can play?

Four.

h .... do you play?

By moving all your pieces to the centre of the board.

i .... does a game last?

Usually about half an hour.

j .... is it so popular?

Because it's easy to learn ... but difficult to play well!

LOOK!

There are two different types of question with *who* (and *what*).

a *Who* is the subject of the sentence:

| subject |

Who is speaking?   no inversion of subject and verb

b *Who* is the object of the sentence:

| object | subject |

Who are you speaking to?   inversion of subject and verb

In the Present (and Past) simple we do **not** use *do/did* in subject questions:

*Who **knows** the answer?*   NOT   ~~Who does know the answer?~~

*What **happened**?*   NOT   ~~What did happen?~~

Subject and object questions

3 Decide if *who* is the subject or object of the questions below. Circle the correct form.

a Who (wants)/ *does want* a cup of coffee?

b Who *won / did win* the football match, last night?

c Who *want / do you want* to go with?

d Who *knows / does know* the right answer?

e Who *already know / do you already know* in this class?

f Who *told / did tell* you the news?

g Who *live / do you live* with?

h Who *lives / does live* in the flat next door?

i Who *smokes / does smoke*?

j Who *broke / did break* my pen?

Present Simple

4 **a)** Read the text about the Wilson sisters.

Jennifer and Rosemary Wilson are twin sisters, and they're both famous ... but they have very different lives!

Jennifer lives in London: she's a well-known TV presenter, and she gets up at 3 a.m. every day to introduce the popular breakfast TV show *Good Morning UK!!* She finishes work at about 10.30 a.m.

Rosemary is a professional tennis player: she now lives in Beverley Hills, USA with her American husband, Ron. Rosemary comes to England two or three times a year to play: she always stays with her sister.

b) Correct the information in the sentences below. Use the information in the text.

1 Jennifer and Rosemary have very similar lives.
 They don't have very similar lives: they have very different lives.

2 Jennifer and Rosemary live in the same country.

....

....

3 Jennifer lives in the United States.

....

....

4 She works in the evening.

....

....

5 Rosemary plays golf.

....

....

....

6 She stays in a hotel when she comes to Britain.

....

....

....

7 They see each other every weekend.

....

....

....

c) Write questions.

1 *Where does Jennifer Wilson live?*
 She lives in London.

2 ....
 .... ?
 At 3 a.m.

3 ....
 .... ?
 At about 10.30 a.m.

4 ....
 .... ?
 In Beverley Hills.

5 ....
 .... ?
 Two or three times a year.

6 ....
 .... ?
 To play tennis.

7 ....
 .... ?
 With her sister.

d) 📼 Listen and check. Practise the pronunciation of the questions.

Short answers

> **LOOK!**
>
> When we answer questions, we often use short answers, like this.
>
> | Question | Short answer | | |
> |---|---|---|---|
> | **Do you** / they play tennis? | Yes, **I / they do.** | or | No, **I / they don't.** |
> | **Does (s)he** like ice-cream? | Yes **(s)he does.** | or | No, **(s)he doesn't.** |

5 **a)** Answer these questions about yourself. Use short answers.

1 Do you like pasta? _Yes, I do._

2 Do you live near the sea? ....

3 Do you smoke? ....

b) Answer these questions about someone you know well (for example your mother or your best friend). Use short answers.

1 Does (s)he wear glasses? ....

2 Does (s)he live near you? ....

3 Does (s)he drive a car? ....

c) Answer these questions about Jennifer and Rosemary Wilson. Read the text again if necessary. Use short answers.

1 Do they live in the same city? ....

2 Do they have the same job? ....

3 Do they often visit each other? ....

4 Do they look similar? ....

Frequency

Adverbs

6 Complete each sentence with a frequency adverb so it is true for you. Be careful to put the adverb in the correct position in the sentence.

always   often   sometimes   occasionally   never

a I ⌐sometimes watch TV in bed.

b I am late for work / school.

c I play computer games.

d I go to the opera.

e I cook a meal for my friends.

f I eat chocolate.

Phrases

> **LOOK!**
>
> | once twice three times four times etc. | a | day week month year |
> |---|---|---|

7 Replace the phrase in **bold** with a frequency phrase. Use the word in brackets ( ) to help you.

a I go to English lessons **on Tuesdays and Thursdays.** I go to English lessons _twice a week_ .... (week)

b We usually go on holiday **in April, in July and in December.** We usually go on holiday .... (year)

c We go swimming **every Sunday.** We go swimming .... (week)

d It's important to visit the dentist **every six months.** It's important to visit the dentist .... (year)

e My friend goes running **on Mondays, Wednesdays, Fridays and Sundays.** My friend goes running .... (week)

f I check my e-mail **in the morning and in the evening.** I check my e-mail .... (day)

g I go to visit my cousin in Bristol **about every four weeks.** I go to visit my cousin in Bristol .... (month)

Vocabulary booster: sports

8 a) What are the sports and activities below?
Use the pictures to help you.

1 S E L L A B B A	*BASEBALL*	
2 Y C C I L G N	_ _ _ _ _ _ _	
3 I N K S I G	_ _ _ _ _	
4 G W I M S M I N	_ _ _ _ _ _ _	
5 C I E - I T A N K S G	_ _ _ - _ _ _ _ _ _	
6 E S H O R - I D N G I R	_ _ _ _ _ - _ _ _ _ _	
7 B L E A T N I N S E T	_ _ _ _ _ _ _ _ _ _	
8 L E B L A K T A B S	_ _ _ _ _ _ _ _ _	
9 G O B N I X	_ _ _ _ _	
10 M I S T C A N G Y S	_ _ _ _ _ _ _ _	
11 L O B V A L E L Y L	_ _ _ _ _ _ _ _ _	

b) 📼 Listen to the spelling and pronunciation
of the words. Practise the pronunciation.

c) Write the names of:

1 **one** sport which needs gloves
boxing..........

2 **four** sports which use a ball
....
....

3 **three** sports which need water, ice or snow
....

4 **two** sports in which you ride something
....

5 **two** sports you do in a gym
....

Vocabulary

Phrases with *go* and *play*

LOOK!

go	+	activity	
		(= **verb** + *-ing*)	*go skiing*
go to the	+	place	*go to the gym*
play	+	sport / game	*play football, play cards*
play the	+	musical instrument	*play the guitar*

9 Put the words in the box in the correct column.

chess gym football guitar cinema
table tennis violin park computer games
shopping beach skiing ice-skating trumpet
piano dancing

go	go to the	play	play the
....	....	*chess*	....
....	....	....	....
....	....	....	....
....	....	....	....

Pronunciation

The /ə/ sound

> **LOOK!**
>
> The word *teacher* has two syllables: teach·er
>
> /ə/
>
> The **first** syllable is stressed (it is stronger and louder).
> The **second** syllable is unstressed. We often pronounce unstressed syllables: /ə/.
>
> The word *Internet* has 3 syllables: In·ter·net
>
> /ə/
>
> The **first** syllable is stressed.
> The **second** syllable is pronounced: /ə/.

10 **a)** 📼 Listen to the words below. Notice the stress on each word. Write /ə/ under the syllable or syllables which are pronounced /ə/.

1 nev·er
....

2 am·bi·tion
....

3 com·put·er
....

4 ex·er·cise
....

5 en·ter·tain
....

6 pro·fes·sion·al
....

7 lei·sure
....

8 foot·bal·ler
....

9 pop·u·lar
....

10 pre·sent·er
....

b) 📼 Listen and practise the pronunciation of the words.

Improve your writing

Punctuation (1)

> **LOOK!**

A B C D	capital letters	We use these with the names of people, towns, countries, languages, and at the beginning of a sentence. *My brother Frank teaches English in Italy.*
.	full stop	We use this at the end of a sentence⊙ *... end of a sentence.*
,	a comma	a We use this to separate things in a list: *She likes eating out, movies, music and dancing.* (before the last item, we use *and* instead of a comma) b We also use a comma to show a short pause: *... in Sydney, the biggest city in Australia, you ...*
'	apostrophe	We use this to show contracted forms, and with possessive *s*: *I'm twenty-six years old.* *When's she arriving?* *We've got a dog and two cats.* *Zoe's friends are in Barcelona.*

11 In the paragraph below:

a) Put a full stop, comma or an apostrophe in the spaces marked _.

b) Change 20 letters into capital letters.

> 'everybody thinks I_m a typical englishwoman,' actress kate thomson told *Go!* magazine. 'I really don_t know why ...'. when she was 18_ kate left england_ she lived first in canada_ then morocco_ where she met french film producer serge roux_ the couple now live in paris with their three children: patrick_ james and lucie_ 'We_re so happy here. It_s nice to have children who can speak both english and french_'

module 2

Past Simple

Regular and irregular verbs

1 Complete the past forms of the verbs below. Use the list on page 148 of the Students' Book to find out which verbs are irregular.

appear	appear<u>ed</u>
drive	d r _ v e
go	we _ _
make	m a _ _
begin	b e g _ n
eat	_ t _
happen	happen _ _
meet	m _ _
buy	bou _ _ t
fall	fe _ _
know	kn _ w
play	play _ _
come	c _ me
feel	fe _ _
live	liv _ _
read	r _ _ d
cost	c _ st
find	f _ _ nd
look	look _ _
take	t _ _ k
die	dı _ _
get	g _ t
lose	lo _ _
write	w r _ te

2 Put the verbs in brackets into the Past Simple.

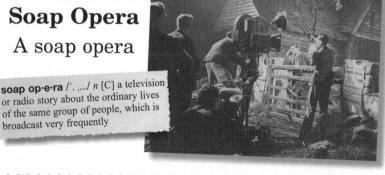

The first TV Soap Opera
A soap opera

soap op·e·ra /'. ,.../ *n* [C] a television or radio story about the ordinary lives of the same group of people, which is broadcast very frequently

The first TV soap opera (a) ....*appeared*.... (*appear*) on American television just after the Second World War. Its name (b) .... (*be*) *Faraway Hill* and it (c) .... (*begin*) on 2nd October 1946. A famous Broadway actress, Flora Campbell, (d) .... (*play*) Karen St. John, a rich New York woman who (e) .... (*go*) to live with her relatives in the country after her husband (f) .... (*die*). She soon (g) .... (*meet*) a handsome young farmer, and of course the two immediately (h) .... (*fall*) in love. Unfortunately, the farmer (i) .... (*be*) already engaged to Karen's cousin, who (j) .... (*know*) nothing about the relationship. When she (k) .... (*find*) out, things (l) .... (*get*) very, very difficult for Karen. The producers of *Faraway Hill* (m) .... (*have*) very little money – each programme (n) .... (*cost*) only $300 – so they (o) .... (*make*) them as quickly as possible. Because there (p) .... (*be*) no time for the actors to learn their words each week, assistants (q) .... (*write*) them on blackboards. Because of this, they often (r) .... (*look*) into the distance with a strange, romantic expression on their faces ... as they (s) .... (*read*) their words from the boards on the other side of the studio!

Negatives and affirmatives

3 Correct these sentences about *Faraway Hill*.

a The first TV soap opera appeared before the Second World War.

It didn't appear before the Second World War. - it appeared after the Second World War.

b It began in October 1936.

....

....

....

c It was about a rich farmer who moved to New York.

....

....

....

d The woman fell in love with her cousin.

....

....

....

e Her lover was married to her cousin.

....

....

....

f The producers of the programme had a lot of money.

....

....

....

g The assistants wrote the actors' words on pieces of paper.

....

....

....

did, *was* or *were* in questions and answers

4 Yesterday evening Ruth had her first date with Oliver. Her younger sister, Emma, is asking her about it.

a) Complete Ruth and Emma's conversation with *was / wasn't, were / weren't* or *did / didn't*.

E: So how (1) ..was.......... your evening with Oliver?

R: It (2) .... good. Yes, very good.

E: Mmm ... where (3) .... you go?

R: To see the new James Bond movie.

E: (4) .... it good?

R: Well, it (5) .... really the kind of film I like, you know, I'm not a James Bond fan, but it (6) .... quite funny.

E: And (7) .... you go anywhere after that?

R: We went to that new bar opposite the cinema – a few of Oliver's friends (8) .... there.

E: (9) .... they nice?

R: The boy, James, (10) .... quite nice, but the two girls (11) .... very friendly – they (12) .... talk to me at all, not a word.

E: That (13) .... very nice! How rude!

R: But, anyway, they (14) .... stay long – they left after about twenty minutes ... and then we stayed and talked for an hour or two ... he (15) .... really, really funny!

E: Mm, very nice! (16) .... he buy you dinner?

R: No ... but he bought me a few drinks ...

E: Mmm, and (17) .... he bring you home in his new sports car?

R: Yes ... why?

E: So, (18) .... he very romantic?

R: Emma, mind your own business!

E: And (19) .... he ask to see you again?

R: Yes, he (20) .... , actually ... now go away!

E: Mmm ... very interesting!

b) 📠 Listen and check your answers.

Time phrases often used in the past

ago

5 Answer at least six questions below about yourself. Use *ago* in your answers.

a When did you first start learning English?
I first started learning English three years ago.

b When did you first learn to write?
....

c When did you first use a computer?
....

d When did you first send an e-mail?
....

e When did you first go abroad?
....

f When did you last watch or listen to the news?
I last watched the news this morning.

g When did you last make a phone call?
....

h When did you last wash your hands?
....

i When did you last watch a film?
....

j When did you last write a letter to a friend?
....

in, at, on

6 Complete the gaps with *in*, *at*, *on* or –.

a My grandmother was born ...*in*........... 1939.

b I'll meet you at the cinema .... 8.30.

c I met Kerry in the street .... last week – she looked very well.

d My mother-in-law usually comes to stay .... Christmas.

e I've got a doctor's appointment .... Friday morning.

f My cat sleeps on my bed .... night.

g Pip often goes abroad .... the winter.

h Bob moved to New York .... the 1970s.

Vocabulary

Words to describe feelings

7 Choose one of the adjectives from the box on page 18 of the Students' Book to complete the sentences below.

a When Amanda didn't come home from her night out, her parents felt very ...*worried*..... .

b The train's an hour late and it's raining!! I'm .... !!

c The night before her birthday, Anna was so .... she couldn't sleep.

d After a terrible day at work, I got home, listened to some music and had a bath. Then I felt more ....

e I wanted a new DVD player for my birthday: but all I got was a stupid computer game. I was really ....

f When I was little, I stole a chocolate bar from a shop: but I felt so .... I couldn't eat it.

g It was a beautiful day: it was sunny and as I walked to work, I was really ....

h The film was nearly three hours long: a lot of people got .... and left before the end.

i I was .... to see David in London: I thought he was in Paris!

j Frank woke up and heard a noise downstairs. He was so .... he couldn't move.

k My new hair cut looked horrible: I was too .... to go out.

l I'm sorry. I lost the CD you lent me. Please don't be ....

m People often feel a little .... before an important exam.

Listen and read

8 **a)** Look at the quiz and try to answer the questions.

Movie Quiz
how much do you know about the movies?

1 *The first film came from:*

    a France   b Australia   c The USA

2 *Hollywood became important for film-making in:*

    a the 1900s   b the 1920s   c the 1930s

3 *The first movies with sound appeared in:*

    a 1917   b 1927   c 1937

4 *Rudolph Valentino was famous as:*

    a a cowboy   b a comedian   c a lover

5 *The actress Greta Garbo originally came from:*

    a Germany   b Russia   c Sweden

6 *The first Disney character was:*

    a Bambi   b Mickey Mouse   c Snow White

7 *The most expensive film of the twentieth century was:*

    a *Star Wars*   b *Batman Forever*   c *Titanic*

8 *The most successful film of the twentieth century was:*

    a *Citizen Kane*   b *Gone with the Wind*   c *Titanic*

9 *They make the most films in:*

    a The USA   b France   c India

10 *People go to the cinema most often in:*

    a The USA   b Lebanon   c India

b) 🖭 Now read and listen to the text on the next page and check your answers.

The Magic of Movies

How much do you know about films?

Did you know ...

- The first film appeared in Paris in 1895. The makers were two French brothers, Louis and Auguste Lumière, and it only lasted a few minutes, (the first <u>full-length</u> film didn't appear until 1905), but movies have been popular ever since.

- Between 1907 and 1913, Hollywood in Southern California became the centre of the American (and international) film industry – the weather was perfect for making films outside!

- Until the late 1920s, movies were silent. Words on the <u>screen</u> told the important parts of the story and in each cinema, a pianist played music at the same time as the film. Great stars of the silent movies included Rudolph Valentino, who was famous as a great lover and the London-born comedian Charlie Chaplin. The great Swedish actress, Greta Garbo, also started her career in silent movies.

- The first 'talkie', a film called *The Jazz Singer* appeared in 1927, and starred Al Jolson. A few years later, the first colour movies appeared.

- Walt Disney designed his first cartoon character, Mickey Mouse, in 1928. Later, Donald Duck appeared, and in 1937 Disney made his first full-length cartoon film, *Snow White and the Seven Dwarfs*.

- The most popular film of 1939, *Gone with the Wind*, starring Clark Gable and Vivien Leigh, was the most successful film of all time until *Titanic* appeared in 1997.

- *Titanic*, starring Leonardo DiCaprio and Kate Winslet, was the most expensive film ever made – it cost $200 million to make. It also made the most money ($1.6 billion in its first year alone) and won the most Oscars of any film (eleven including 'Best Film').

- However, <u>film critics</u> often choose the 1941 film, *Citizen Kane*, starring Orson Welles, as the best film ever.

- You may think that the United States is the centre of the movie world, but that isn't completely true. The Indian film industry makes many more films each year than the Americans do (850 compared to 570 in the USA); the Lebanese go to the cinema much more often (35 times a year on average, compared to just 4 times a year in the US) and Belarussia has more cinemas per million people than the USA!

Glossary

A *full-length film* lasts more than an hour.
The *screen* is what you look at when you watch a film.
A *film critic* is an expert who writes about films in a newspaper or magazine.

Spelling

-ed endings

9 **a)** Look at the spelling rules in the language summary on page 150 of the Students' Book.

b) Use the rules to write the past simple forms of these regular verbs.

1 believe ....
2 cry ....
3 continue ....
4 drop ....
5 hurry ....
6 use ....
7 marry ....
8 phone ....
9 stop ....
10 study ....
11 try ....
12 dance ....

Pronunciation

-ed endings

> **LOOK!**
>
> Normally the -ed ending does **not** make an extra syllable.
>
> 🔊 Listen:
> push = 1 syllable
> an·swer = 2 syllables
>
> pushed = 1 syllable
> an·swered = 2 syllables
>
> But if the verb ends with the sound /t/ or /d/, there is an extra syllable, pronounced /ɪd/.
>
> 🔊 Listen:
> wait = 1 syllable
> end = 1 syllable
>
> wait·ed = 2 syllables
> end·ed = 2 syllables

10 **a)** 🔊 Listen to these past forms. Write down the number of syllables you hear.

1 studied ......2......
2 listened ....
3 wanted ....
4 compared ....
5 tried ....
6 used ....
7 loved ....
8 hated ....
9 remembered ....
10 stayed ....
11 acted ....
12 enjoyed ....

b) 🔊 Listen again and repeat.

Linkers: *but, so, because, then*

11 Correct the linker to make the sentences logical.

a I'm really tired ......~~but~~...... I'm going to bed.
   so

b I couldn't buy anything ....~~so~~........ I forgot my purse.

c He's broken his arm ....~~because~~........ he can't play football.

d First you put in the cassette, ...~~but~~...... you press this button here.

e We got an expensive new computer this week, ...~~so~~.......... we're having a lot of problems with it.

f The new teacher is very nice, ...~~then~~.......... she's very strict about homework.

g It's terribly hot on the beach ......~~because~~...... we're taking the children home.

h His boss was angry with him ....~~so~~........ he was late for work three times in a week.

i Finish your drink: ....~~but~~........ we must go home.

module 3

can / can't

1 **a)** Rewrite the sentences replacing the phrase in **bold** with *can* or *can't*.

1 **Is it possible** to borrow your dictionary?
   Can I borrow your dictionary ?

2 My sister **is able to** speak three languages perfectly.
   ....
   ....

3 I'm sorry, you **don't have permission to** bring your dog in here.
   ....
   ....

4 Nowadays, **it is possible for you to** buy cheap aeroplane tickets on the Internet.
   ....
   ....

5 Bad news: **it's impossible for Renate to** come to the party on Saturday.
   ....
   ....

6 **Are you able to** read Russian? I don't understand this.
   ....
   ....

7 'I'm sorry **we're not able to** answer the phone at the moment: please leave a message ...'
   ....
   ....

8 'Is it possible for us to' have a table by the window?'
   ....
   ....

b) 📼 Listen to the cassette. Practise saying the correct sentences.

have to / don't have to

2 Which of these things do you have to do at school/at work? Which don't you have to do? Write sentences.

> start at 8.00 in the morning   wear a uniform
> go to work on Saturdays   work / study in the evening
> sit at a desk all day   do a lot of writing
> go to meetings   make phone calls all day
> be polite all the time   concentrate hard

a *I have to start work at 8.00 in the morning.* ....
b ....
   ....
c ....
   ....
d ....
   ....
e ....
   ....
f ....
   ....
g ....
   ....
h ....
   ....
i ....
   ....
j ....
   ....

can / can't / have to / don't have to

3 Ben is going to take his driving test soon. Complete the conversation with the correct form of *have to* or *can*.

BEN: Is it true that there are two driving tests?

INSTRUCTOR: That's right: you (a) .....have to......... take a written test and a practical – that's where you're on the road with the examiner.

BEN: I think I prefer the second one. (b) .... I take the practical test first, please?

INSTRUCTOR: No, I'm sorry. You (c) .... take the practical test until you've passed the written.

BEN: Hmm ... Is the written test very difficult?

INSTRUCTOR: No, not really. There are fifty questions, but the good news is you (d) .... answer all of them correctly. You (e) .... get 45 correct answers, so you (f) .... make a few mistakes and still pass.

BEN: I see. (g) .... you give me some advice about how to prepare for the written exam?

INSTRUCTOR: Try to learn all the rules of the road! But there are thousands, so you (h) .... remember everything at once – you (i) .... study a little bit every day.

BEN: OK. How about the practical exam?

INSTRUCTOR: Well, on the day, the examiner (j) .... see your driving licence, so don't forget it !! Then he asks you to read a number plate to check you (k) .... see OK.

BEN: That sounds easy ... (l) .... I take my test straight away?

INSTRUCTOR: Impossible! You (m) .... learn to park first – you won't pass if you (n) .... park your car!

should / shouldn't

4 You are having dinner with people you don't know well. Which of the things below *should* you do and which *shouldn't* you do in your culture?

a You .....shouldn't........ speak with your mouth full.

b You .... wait for the others before you start eating.

c You .... eat with your fingers.

d You .... eat with your elbows on the table.

e You .... make a noise when you drink something.

f You .... put the knife in your mouth.

g You .... use a spoon for soup.

h You .... put your knife and fork on the plate when you finish.

Short answers with modal verbs *can*, *should*, *have to*

5 **a)** When we answer questions with modal verbs, we often use short answers, like this.

> Can I / you / (s)he / it / we / they come?
> Yes, I / you / (s)he / it / we / they can.
> No, I / you / (s)he / it / we / they can't.
>
> Should I / you / (s)he / it / we / they go?
> Yes, I / you / (s)he / it / we / they should.
> No, I / you / (s)he / it / we / they shouldn't.
>
> Do I / you / we / they have to go?
> Yes, I / you / we / they do.
> No, I / you / we / they don't.
>
> Does (s)he / it have to go?
> Yes, (s)he / it does.
> No, (s)he / it doesn't.

LOOK!

b) Complete the dialogues with an appropriate short answer.

1 Can you and Roberto come for a coffee with us after class?
No, we can't. .... I'm sorry - we have to go home.

2 Do I have to pay for the room now?
.... You can pay us when you leave if you prefer.

3 Should we phone your mother to tell her we're going to be late?
.... Here's my phone.

4 Can we leave our coats here during the break?
.... But don't leave any money in your pockets.

5 Do you think I should send a photograph with the application form?
.... It's better if they can see what you look like.

6 My son is six years old. Do I have to buy a ticket for him as well?
.... It costs half the price of an adult ticket.

7 Do you have to get up early tomorrow?
.... In fact, I can stay in bed as long as I want!

8 Can you speak Japanese ?
.... I lived there for four years, so I learned quite a lot.

Prepositions

6 Choose the correct preposition to complete each sentence.

a If you don't know a phone number, you can look it *up* .... in the phone book.

b I can't think .... an explanation for what happened.

c Jon is going to phone the cinema to find .... what time the film starts.

d Clara tried to explain .... the other students what the word meant.

e I gave him my address, and Philip wrote it .... on a piece of paper.

f People have many different reasons .... learning a language.

g Almost everybody in my country studies English .... university.

h Mario sits .... the library every afternoon, studying for his exams.

i It's very difficult to learn a language .... your own: I think you should join a class.

j If you don't know the answer .... a question ... guess!!

19

Vocabulary booster: things in a school

7 **a)** Look at the picture below. Label the numbered items with the correct word from the box.

notebook   file   hole punch   rubber   video recorder   board rubber
waste bin   cassette player   overhead projector   pencil case   bookcase
ruler   whiteboard   pencil sharpener

3 ....

4 ....

1 ....

2 ....

5 ....

6 ....

7 ....

8 ....

9 ....

10 ....

11 ....

12 ....

13 ....

14 ....

Hello Class A

pencils

b) 📼 Listen and check. Practise saying the words.

c) Put the items into one of the boxes below.

Uses electricity	Doesn't use electricity – usually metal	Doesn't use electricity – not metal
cassette player	hole punch	rubber
....	....	....
....	....	....
....	....	....
....	....	....
....	....	....

Vocabulary

Wordbuilding

8 **a)** Write the nouns from these verbs. Use a dictionary if necessary.

communicate	*communication*
improve	....
imagine	....
advise	....
interrupt	....
practise	....
pronounce	....
explain	....

b) 📼 Listen to the words and mark the stress.

c) Complete the sentences so that the meaning is the same.

1 His work really improved when he changed schools.
There was a big *..improvement..* in his work when he changed schools.

2 Phones, faxes and e-mails make it easier to communicate with other people.
Phones, faxes and e-mails mean better .... with other people.

3 When you read a good book, you have to imagine.
When you read a good book, you have to use your ....

4 Could you advise me about which computer to buy?
Could you give me some .... about which computer to buy?

5 It's difficult to work hard when people interrupt you a lot.
It's difficult to work hard when there are a lot of ....

6 You need to practise a lot before you can drive well.
You need a lot of .... before you can drive well.

7 How do you pronounce this word?
What is the .... of this word?

8 Nobody can explain what happened that night.
Nobody can give an .... of what happened that night.

Collocations

9 Below is a summary of *What's the secret of successful language learning?* from page 25 of the Students' Book. Complete the gaps using verbs from the box.

~~learn~~   have   get   make   work   understand

Alastair says that if you want to (a).*learn*............ a language, confidence is very important. You also have to (b)...................... hard, and not (c)...................... frustrated if you don't (d)...................... very much progress. You should try to develop an ear for language; this will help you to (e)...................... what people are saying much more easily. Of course it's also important to (f)...................... a good teacher!

~~study~~   become   forget   listen   praise   read

Teresa advises her students to (g).*study*............ grammar, (h)...................... newspapers, magazines etc. and (i)...................... to the radio, pop songs etc. You need a teacher to help you, because people often (j)...................... what they've learned if they don't have someone to 'push' them. She never forgets to (k)...................... her learners when they are successful. Many of them now speak English better than her and have (l)...................... English teachers themselves!

Pronunciation

How to pronounce the letter 'a'

10 **a)** 🔊 There are a number of different ways to pronounce the letter 'a'. Listen:

/æ/ e.g.: **have to**	/ɑː/ e.g.: **can't**	/eɪ/ e.g.: **make**
have to	can't	make
....	....	....
....	....	....
....	....	....
....	....	....

b) Here are some other words from module 3. Put the <u>underlined</u> letter 'a' in the correct column according to its pronunciation.

communic**a**te   pr**a**ctise   ex**a**m   t**a**ke   m**a**rk
h**a**rd   mist**a**ke   g**a**me   Sp**a**nish   educ**a**tion
f**a**r   underst**a**nd

c) 🔊 Listen and check. Practise saying the words.

Improve your writing

Writing a paragraph

11 **1)** Read the sentences below and put them into the correct order.

a That's why I think that everyone should learn at least one foreign language from the age of eight.

b Also, children are less worried about making mistakes when they learn than adults.

c Nowadays, communication between people from different countries is more important than ever before.

d The main reason for this is that many people say it gets harder to learn a new language as you get older.

1 ....   2 ....   3 ....

4 ....

2) Which sentence:

a introduces the topic?   ....

b gives the writer's opinion?   ....

c gives a reason?   ....

d gives another reason?   ....

3) Write a similar paragraph yourself about one of the topics below. Use the language in the box to help you.

- the school-leaving age
- military service
- going to university
- learning to drive a car
- learning to use a computer

Nowadays, ... is more important than ever before,
That's why I think that ...
I think that everyone should ...
The main reason for this is that ...
Also...

Spelling

Finding mistakes

12 **a)** Read the paragraph about Stefanie below. There is a total of ten spelling mistakes. Find and correct the mistakes.

pleased
Stefanie is very ~~pleasd~~ - she has wan a competition at her college. The price is a two-month language corse in Edinburgh.
She will have English lessons for three hours evry morning, but she wants to now the best way to emprove her English outside her lessons. Her freinds, familly and teachers have lots of advise!

b) Check your answers by reading the text about Stefanie on page 26 of the Students' Book, or by looking in the Answer Key.

module 4

Present Continuous

1 Put the verb in brackets into the correct form of the Present Continuous: positive, negative, question or short answer.

a A: Good evening. _Are you enjoying_ (you / enjoy) yourselves?

   B: Oh, yes! _We're having_ (we / have) a fantastic time, thank you!

b A: I'm sorry .... (I / drive) too fast for you?

   B: Yes, ... Could you slow down a bit?

c A: What .... (you / do)?

   B: There's a film on TV, but .... (I / not / watch) it really.

d A: What's the problem?

   B: .... (look for) my keys. .... (you / sit) on them?

   A: Oh, yes, here they are, sorry!

e It's Sunday, so Virginia .... (not / work) today. She .... (spend) some time at home for a change.

Present Simple or Present Continuous?

2 Underline the correct form: Present Simple or Present Continuous.

a A: What languages *are you speaking* / <u>*do you speak*</u>?

   B: English, French and Italian.

b A: [BANG] Ow!!!

   B: What's the matter – what *do you do* / *are you doing*?

c A: What's that song *you listen to* / *you're listening to*?

   B: It's called 'Angels'. Good, isn't it?

d A: What *are you reading* / *do you read*?

   B: It's an article about holidays in Switzerland.

e A: *Do you smoke* / *Are you smoking*?

   B: No, thank you. I stopped smoking two years ago.

f A: Why *are you laughing* / *do you laugh*?

   B: It's your face. You look so funny!!

g A: *Does your brother play* / *Is your brother playing* any sport?

   B: Yes. Football in the winter, tennis in the summer and swimming all year.

h A: Paul. PAUL!! *Are you listening* / *Do you listen* to me?

   B: Hmm? What? Sorry?

State and action verbs

3 Tick (✔) the sentences which are correct. Put a cross (✘) by the sentences which are wrong, and correct them.

> **LOOK!**
> Some verbs describe things which stay the same. These are called **state** verbs.
> We don't usually use them in the continuous form.
> **Verbs of feeling:** *like, love, hate*
> **Verbs of thinking:** *believe, know, understand*
>
> Other verbs describe things that can happen quickly. These are called **action** verbs. We can use them either in simple or continuous forms.
> *He's driving home.*
> *He drives home every day.*

1 Are you liking coffee? ✘
   Do you like coffee?

2 Do you like coffee? ✔
   ....

3 I'm not believing you!
   ....

4 Do you want a drink?
   ....

5 I'm not understanding him.
   ....

6 I'm hating cold weather!
   ....

7 I don't understand Turkish.
   ....

8 I'm not knowing her name.
   ....

Present Continuous for future arrangements

4 **a)** Look at the family calendar for next week. Write sentences about the four family members, like this:

Steve isn't working on Monday. He's playing squash with Andy at 10.30.

....
....
....
....
....
....
....
....
....
....
....
....
....
....

	Steve	Judy	Oliver	Florence
Mon 7	No work! Squash with Andy 10.30	work		swimming
Tues 8	to Manchester for the day. Train at 06.45	doctor's at 09.15	football at 16.00	
Wed 9		work	to Tom's house after school	
Thurs 10	cinema with Jan and Chris (Steve's mum to babysit)			
Fri 11		meet Alison for lunch - 13.00	meeting cousins in the park at 14.30	
Sat 12				
Sun 13	lunch with grandparents at 12.00			

b) 📼 Practise saying the sentences on the tape.

Vocabulary booster: special occasions

5 **a)** Look at the pictures and label the numbered items with the correct word from the box.

| presents   paper plates   candles   someone making a wish   glasses |
| the host and hostess   birthday cake   guests   decorations   paper cups |
| sandwiches   cards |

1 ....

2 ....

3 ....

4 ....

5 ....

6 ....

7 ....

8 ....

9 ....

10 ....

11 ....

12 ....

b) 📼 Listen to the pronunciation of the words on the tape. Practise saying the words.

Vocabulary

Things people do on special occasions

6 Choose the correct word from the box to complete the sentences.

> dress   have (x 3)   stay   buy   visit   send
> make   spend   give   go

a   At the Carnival, many people *dress* .... up in colourful clothes.

b   It was your cousin's birthday yesterday. Did you remember to .... her a card?

c   During the week, I have to be at home by 11, but at the weekend I can .... out late.

d   People in Britain often .... relatives on Christmas Day. After lunch, they often .... their presents to each other.

e   At the end of the course, our class have decided to .... out for a meal together.

f   I don't feel well today. I'm going to .... the day off work.

g   It's Valentine's Day tomorrow: don't forget to .... some flowers for your wife!

h   Charlie's mum is going to .... a special cake for his birthday.

i   In our family, we always .... a special meal at home on New Year's Eve.

j   It's Samantha's 21st birthday next week. She's going to .... a really big party.

k   We always .... a lot of money over the New Year: that's why we can't go away in January!

Listen and read

7 **a)** 📻 Read and listen to the texts on the next page about three different religious festivals. In which festival do people:

1   clean and decorate their homes?
2   throw water at people in the street?
3   try to understand the problems of the poor?
4   have a special basket of food?
5   not eat between morning and evening?
6   buy new clothes?
7   put bright lights in their homes?

b) Read again and listen to the texts on the tape. Answer these questions.

1   Are Islamic festivals at the same time each year?
2   Which month is Ramadan?
3   What does the 'blessing basket' contain?
4   Which meal is very important to Poles at Easter?
5   In which country is Diwali celebrated?
6   How long is the festival of Diwali?
7   Which Goddess is it the festival of?

Religious festivals around the world

Islamic festivals - Ramadan

Because the Islamic religion uses a calendar based on the moon, not the sun, the exact date of religious festivals changes from year to year. The Islamic Calendar begins with the *hijra*, the year when Mohammed left the city of Mecca for Medina. The New Year is a time for peaceful prayer for most Muslim people. Every year in the month of Ramadan - the ninth month of the Islamic calendar - all Muslims <u>fast</u> from early morning until evening.

By living without everyday comforts, even for a short time, a fasting person better understands the life of poor people who are hungry, and also grows in his or her spiritual life.

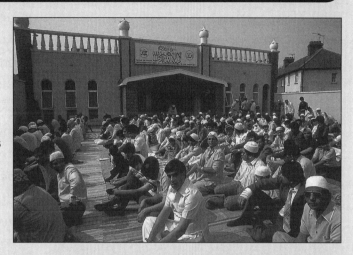

Easter in Poland

In Poland, there are many customs at Easter: for example, the 'blessing basket', containing (among other things) coloured eggs, bread, salt, and white sausages. Everything in the basket has a meaning: the eggs represent Christ, the bread, salt and sausages good health and enough money in the coming year. The family Easter breakfast on Sunday morning is as important as Christmas dinner for Poles. And there is one more Polish tradition connected with Easter Monday: 'watering'. People throw water at each other, and this is a wish for good health, too. Even strangers on the street are not safe from a bath of cold water on Easter Monday!

A Hindu festival - Diwali

The festival of Diwali is one of the most important religious festivals in India. It lasts for five days around the end of October. It is the festival of Laxmi, the Goddess who, in the Hindu religion, brings peace and prosperity.

Preparations for the festival begin several weeks before the festival itself. People clean and decorate their homes, prepare special food and buy new clothes and jewellery to welcome the Goddess into their homes. All over India, people light up their homes with oil lamps and colourful lights.

The celebrations take place on the darkest night of the lunar month, Amavasya. In the evening, fireworks fill the sky to make Diwali a true 'Festival of Light'.

Glossary
fast = to eat no food or drink.

Improve your writing

A letter of invitation

8 Write out the letter below with correct layout, capital letters and punctuation. Use the letter on page 38 of the Students' Book to help you.

10 fife road norton
october 7th

dear tony

sorry i haven't written for so long but i've been really busy with the new job I hope you're well and still enjoying life at university the main reason i'm writing is to tell you that valerie and I are staying at uncle frank's villa in spain for the winter holidays would you like to come and stay for a few days the villa is in a really beautiful place very near the beach you can fly to malaga airport and get a bus from there can you give me a ring to tell me if you're interested our new phone number is 01804 742 3812 we'd love to see you see you soon

mark

Spelling

-ing forms

9 Look at the spelling rules on page 00 of the Students' Book. Tick (✔) the correct spellings and correct the ones that are wrong.

celebrateing   ✗ *celebrating*

cooking   ....

driveing   ....

getting   ....

giveing   ....

inviteing   ....

liveing   ....

putting   ....

studying   ....

taking   ....

wearring   ....

writeing   ....

Pronunciation

/ð/ and /θ/

10 a) 📼 Listen to the underlined sounds in these words and phrases from module 4 and put them in the correct column: /ð/ or /θ/

Mo<u>th</u>er's Day   Fa<u>th</u>er's Day   bir<u>th</u>day
twenty-fif<u>th</u>   four<u>th</u>   <u>th</u>irty-first   <u>th</u>e o<u>th</u>er day
<u>th</u>e day before yesterday   <u>th</u>ese days
in <u>th</u>ose days   your good heal<u>th</u>
<u>Th</u>anks for coming!

/ð/	/θ/
Mother's Day	

b) 📼 Listen again and practise saying the words.

module 5

Comparatives and superlatives

Comparative forms

1 **a)** Read the profiles of Paul Chang and Mike 'The Monster' Morton. Use the adjectives in brackets to complete the questions and answers below.

	PAUL CHANG	MIKE 'THE MONSTER' MORTON
Age:	19	36
Height:	1.85m	1.78m
Strength:	Very fast	Slow
Weakness:	Not very experienced	Very experienced
Weight:	80kg	95kg
Aggression factor:	80%	95%
Power rating:	7/10	9/10
Popularity	☺☺☺	☺

Who is...

1 *(old)* .....older?.....
...Mike is older than Paul.....

2 *(young)* ....?
....

3 *(tall)* ....?
....

4 *(fast)* ....?
....

5 *(experienced)* ....?
....

6 *(slow)* ....?
....

7 *(heavy)* ....?
....

8 *(aggressive)* ....?
....

9 *(powerful)* ....?
....

10 *(popular)* ....?
....

b) 📼 Listen to the tape. Practise saying the sentences.

Superlative forms

2 Put the adjectives into the superlative form.

a The *tallest*.................. *(tall)* US President was Abraham Lincoln, who was 1m 93, and the .... *(old)* was Ronald Reagan, who was 69 when he became President in 1981.

b The .... *(fast)* winner of a London Marathon was the Portuguese runner Antonio Pinto – fourteen minutes better than the .... *(quick)* woman, Ingrid Kristiansen from Norway.

c Sultan Hassanal Bolkiah – Sultan of the Arab state of Brunei, is the world's .... *(rich)* monarch. Many people think that Queen Elizabeth of Great Britain is the .... *(wealthy)* female ruler.

d Elvis Presley – who died in 1977– was probably the .... *(popular)* singer of all time. He always said that the .... *(important)* person in his life was his mother.

e Queen Jane had the .... *(short)* time on the throne of any English Queen – just five days! King Louis XIV of France was King for the .... *(long)* time: 72 years!

3 🔘 Here are some famous sayings which contain a comparative or superlative adjective. Listen to the sayings and underline the comparative and superlative forms.

a

Democracy is the <u>worst</u> form of government … apart from all the others.

Winston Churchill

b

The reason I wanted to be an actress was to play people much more interesting than I am, and to say things much more intelligent than anything I could think of myself.

Actress Prunella Scales

c

All animals are equal, but some are more equal than others.

George Orwell in Animal Farm

d

Good, better, the best
Never let it rest
Until good is better
And better is the best

Unknown teacher

e

It was the best of times, it was the worst of times.

Charles Dickens: beginning of 'A Tale of Two Cities'

f

Being funny is much more difficult than being clever.

Editor of a comedy magazine

Prepositions in comparative phrases: *as, than, from, like, in, to*

4 Complete the sentences with *as, than, from, like, in* or *to*.

a Marie's dress is very similar *to*............. mine.

b She has the same taste in clothes .... me.

c Anna is older .... she looks.

d Tom always seems to have more money .... everyone else.

e Do you look .... your parents?

f Who's the youngest person .... your family?

g Our lives today are very different .... the way our grandparents lived.

h What's your parents' house .... ?

Describing what people look like

Questions about appearance

5 Write the questions for these answers about Donna.

a *How old is she?*..
She's in her twenties.

b .... ?
She's very athletic and friendly-looking.

c .... ?
About 1m 75.

d .... ?
She's black.

e .... ?
It's long.

f .... ?
They're dark brown.

is or *has got?*

6 Complete the gaps with *is* ('s) / *are* or *has* ('s) / *have* ('ve) *got*.

a My grandmother *.is.*................... in her seventies, but she .... a very young face. She .... lovely teeth and skin and she .... (not) any white hair!

d My dad .... a moustache, but he (not) .... a beard any more – he shaved it off a few weeks ago!

b My brothers and sisters .... very similar to look at – they .... all very pale and they .... green eyes and red hair.

e Joe .... like his father – he .... very tall and slim.

c The baby .... only a few days old, but she .... lots and lots of hair.

Vocabulary

Describing appearances

7 Use the clues to complete the grid below. The words all come from the text 'You're Gorgeous' on page 41 of the Students' Book.

1 Eighteenth-century ladies – and men – often wore a .... on their head. (3 letters)

2 Physically strong and good at sport. (8 letters)

3 You are this if you have a lot of courage. (5 letters)

4 When your skin goes brown because of the sun, you have one of these. (6 letters)

5 In the times of Queen Elizabeth I, fashionable ladies wanted their faces to be this colour! (5)

6 You describe someone who wears good clothes as *well-* .... (7 letters)

7 Using a good shampoo can help you to have .... hair! (5 letters)

8 It's between your head and your shoulders! (4 letters)

9 For skin colour, the opposite of dark. (4 letters)

10 Thin, in an attractive way. (4 letters)

11 People put this on their face to look more attractive. (4 letters, 2 letters)

12 People put this liquid on their skin: it has a pleasant smell. (7 letters)

			W	I	G		
2			H				
3			A				
4			T				
5			I				
6			S				
7			H				
8			E				
9			L				
10			I				
11			K				
12			E				
			?				

look

8 Use an expression from the box to complete these sentences.

> looking forward to ~~Look, ...~~ look for
> have a look   Look!   look at   look up   look like
> look out of   -looking

1 *Look, ...* .... I'm sorry to bring you this bad news, but you failed your exams.

2 He was a very good .... man, but he wasn't very intelligent.

3 A: My brother's an artist.
    B: Really! Can I .... at his paintings?

4 Could you help me .... my bag? I can't find it anywhere.

5 .... That man's wearing pink and green trousers.

6 I don't .... my sister. She's got fair hair and blue eyes, and I've got dark hair and brown eyes.

7 I'm really .... my summer holidays – this year we're going to visit my aunt in Tuscany.

8 Our dog loves to .... the window when he travels in the car.

9 You should .... the word in a dictionary if you don't understand it.

10 Stella loves to .... herself in the mirror.

Vocabulary booster: parts of the face and body

9 **a)** Label the pictures.

1 ....

2 ....

3 ....

4 ....

5 ....

6 ....

7 ....

8 ....

9 ....

10 ....

11 ....

12 ....

13 ....

14 ....

15 ....

16 ....

17 ....

18 ....

b) 🔊 Listen and practise the pronunciation of the words.

c) How many does a person usually have? Write the words from part **a)** next to the correct number below.

1 *head*........ , ... , ... , ... ,

.... , ... , ...

2 .... , ... , ... , ... , ... ,

.... , ...

10 .... , ...

32 ....

Uncountable! ....

Improve your writing

Writing a description

10 **a)** Read the description a student wrote of someone in her family. Which sentence talks about:

1 who the person is, and the writer's relationship to her? *E*..............

2 her general appearance? ....

3 her build and height? ....

4 her eyes? ....

5 her hair? ....

6 her age? ....

A
> She's a very attractive little girl – she always looks happy and she's got a lovely smile.

B
> Her eyes are blue, just like her father's.

C
> She's about average height for her age ... and she's quite slim.

D
> She's got beautiful, blonde hair ... and it's her natural colour!

E
> Louise is my youngest cousin, and she lives not far from my family.

F
> She'll be ten next birthday.

b) Make some notes about someone you know well, or someone in your family. Write a paragraph using the suggested order in part **a)**.

Useful phrases

X is my ... , and (s)he lives ...
(S)he's a very .... man / woman / girl / boy and (s)he's got a lovely ...
(S)he's got .... hair / eyes.
His/Her eyes are ... / and (s)he's got long/short, dark/blond hair.
(S)he's about ... tall / about average height.
(S)he's ... years old / (S)he'll be ... next birthday.

Pronunciation

Different ways of pronouncing the letter 'o'

11 **a)** 🔲 There are a number of different ways to pronounce the letter 'o'. Listen:

/ɔː/ e.g.: *more*	/əʊ/ e.g.: *most*	/ɒ/ e.g.: *got*
more	most	got

b) 🔲 Listen to the pronunciation of the words below. In each pair, is the sound in **bold** the same or different?

1 both   important   *different*....

2 old   slow   *the same*....

3 morning   dog   ....

4 toe   nose   ....

5 modern   photograph   ....

6 short   gorgeous   ....

7 popular   **or**ganised   ....

8 local   strong   ....

9 sport   **your**   ....

10 hope   so   ....

c) 🔲 Listen again and practise saying the words.

Spelling

Double letters

12 Below there are twenty words from the module. Eleven of them should have a double instead of a single letter. Mark and correct them as in the example.

beter	*better*........	midle-aged	....
similar	....	personality	....
remember	....	well-dresed	....
slimer	....	glases	....
prety	....	beautiful	....
diferent	....	old-fashioned	....
bigest	....	taned	....
shiny	....	apearance	....
atractive	....	parents	....

module 6

Intentions and wishes

going to and planning to

1 Rearrange the words to make complete sentences.

a   a new computer - you - planning - Are - to buy - ?
   Are you planning to buy
   a new computer?

b   to spend - she's - going - with her family - Lucy - the Summer - says - .
   ....
   ....

c   aren't planning - any - more children - John and his wife - to have - .
   ....
   ....

d   Caroline - after she finishes - a job - is planning - to look for - her exams - .
   ....
   ....

e   to see - are - Which film - going - this evening - you - ?
   ....
   ....

f   is planning - true - Is it - soon - to retire - that - the President - ?
   ....
   ....

g   the school - organise - this Sunday - a barbecue - Is - going to - ?
   ....
   ....

going to, planning to, would like to, would prefer to

2 Read the newspaper column. Choose the phrases from the box to fill the gaps.

> ~~going to~~   He's   I would   planning to   not planning
> I'm planning   is going   to retire   prefer to

Seen and heard

The best of this week's celebrity gossip

by **Stella Renuzzi**

Glamorous actress, Sophie de Roy, has said that she is in love with Argentinian dancer Hector Castagni. 'He's the perfect man for me,' she told me, 'It's not easy being a single girl, but I hope that's (a) *going to* .... change soon.' 'Sophie and I are both very young,' said Castagni in an interview with KO magazine. 'I would (b) .... wait for a few years before we make any important decisions. I'm (c) .... to get married till I'm 30.'

Ex-footballer Jim Norton is in Hollywood hoping for a career in movies. And the good news for Jim is that he has found his first movie role – (d) .... going to play the part of 'Badger' – a violent criminal – in the new Mo Amos film, *Gun Runner*. 'I don't think there's a big difference between acting and playing football,' he said to me, 'so I'm (e) .... move here to help my movie career.'

Angry that his last film *Smash!!* did not win the Academy Award, film director Donald Braine has said that he's going (f) .... from show business. 'If no one likes my films, that's not my problem,' he said. 'The film world is not important to me. I'm more interested in my new restaurant (also called *Smash!!*).' And he has more news:
'(g) .... to open another restaurant (*Smash!! 2*) in Los Angeles next year,' he says.

Holly Pratelli – star of the TV Soap Opera *Hope Street* (h) .... to leave the series. She says it's because she doesn't like her new co-star, Chuck Ryder. 'I don't think he's handsome at all,' she told me. 'One day, (i) .... like to have a big romantic scene with British actor Roy Thinn – he's gorgeous!!'

Glossary
gossip = conversation or writing about other people's behaviour and private lives

35

Predictions

will and *won't*

3 Put *will* or *won't* in the best place in the sentences.

a It be difficult to find accommodation – there aren't many tourists at this time of year. *—won't*

b Do you think we be able to buy tickets when we get there ?

c I'm sorry, but there be any time for us to have lunch.

d You be all right if I go out for a couple of hours?

e I'm going to Michelle's party on Sunday. You be there too?

f Don't worry. I'm sure there be any problems getting a visa.

g How long it take for us to get there?

h There be any food at your party?

Short answers with *will*, *won't* and *going to*

> **LOOK!**
>
> Will you / (s)he /it / we / they be here tomorrow?
>   Yes, I / (s)he / it / we / they will.
>   No, I / (s)he / it / we / they won't.
>
> Are you / we / they going to be there?
>   Yes, I am.
>   Yes, we / you / they are.
>   No, I'm not.
>   No, we're / you're / they're not.
>
> Is (s)he / it going to be there?
>   Yes, (s)he / it is.
>   No, (s)he / it isn't.

4 Write in the correct short answer.

a Will Antonella be at the party on Friday? Yes, *she will.*

b Are you going to say sorry? No, ...

c Is it going to be a nice day? Yes, ...

d Will you be at home if I phone you at 10? No, ...

e Are Jill and Rory going to come with us? No, ...

f Are you going to see Frank this afternoon? Yes, ...

g Will it take a long time to get to the airport? No, ...

h Will you be here next month? Yes, ...

i Is Frederick going to take the exam? No, ...

j Is it going to rain? No, ...

k Will your friends be here for a long time? No, ...

Pronunciation

'll, *will* and *won't*

5 a) Listen to how we pronounce *'ll*, *will* and *won't*.

I'll: I'll go, I'll see, I'll have

will: Will you be ...?, Will there be ...?, Yes, I will

won't: I won't, It won't happen, They won't go

b) Listen to the tape and complete the sentences below.

1 *I'll* .... see you tomorrow.

2 .... be at home tomorrow.

3 .... be at home later?

4 Yes, ...

5 .... be there?

6 No, ...

7 .... be here soon.

8 .... be long.

c) Listen again and practise saying the sentences on the tape.

Vocabulary

Holidays

6 **a)** Choose an adjective from the box to match one of the definitions below.

crowded fantastic luxurious tasty lively polluted disgusting boiling ~~lovely~~ peaceful relaxing terrible wet windy sandy

1 beautiful and enjoyable
   lovely..

2 very comfortable, beautiful and expensive
   ....

3 extremely hot
   ....

4 very unpleasant, making you feel sick
   ....

5 cheerful and active
   ....

6 pleasant and making you feel calm and comfortable
   ....

7 damaged by dangerous chemicals or gases, etc.
   ....

8 when the wind is very strong
   ....

9 good to eat or drink
   ....

10 very bad or unpleasant
   ....

11 extremely good
   ....

12 too full of people or things
   ....

13 calm and quiet
   ....

14 covered in sand
   ....

15 rainy
   ....

b) Complete the gaps with an adjective from the box in part a.

1 'Did you have a good holiday?'
   'Oh yes! It was absolutely *fantastic*.....!'

2 I really enjoyed the food when we visited Japan. We had a dish called *teriyaki* which was very ....

3 My grandmother was a .... person: everyone in the village liked her.

4 Always take an umbrella when you go out: the weather is often .... in October.

5 It was so .... during the night that a number of trees fell down.

6 At the weekend, the beach got so ...., there was nowhere for us to sit.

7 San Clemento is a very .... town: there are hundreds of bars and restaurants, and plenty of night life.

8 Don't try to walk anywhere in the afternoon – the temperature is sometimes 40° – absolutely ....!

9 For me, there is nothing more .... than a sauna.

10 Unfortunately, the lake near the industrial plant is now so .... that all the fish have died.

11 We stayed in a cabin in the mountain, far from any roads or towns. It was very ....

12 The Hotel Metropole is a five-star hotel; one of the most .... hotels in the city.

13 If you walk down the path, there's a .... beach where you can go swimming or just relax.

14 We had a very enjoyable time in Dublin, but unfortunately the weather was .... – cold and wet!

15 This fish is over a week old. It smells ....!

Listen and read

7 📼 Read and listen to the information about holiday offers. Find the answers to the questions below:

a Which is the cheapest holiday destination?

....

b If you want information about cheap flights to Hong Kong, what number should you phone?

....

c How long is the holiday in Sorrento?

....

d Which hotel do you stay at in Boston?

....

e How much does the holiday in Spain cost?

....

f On what date does the holiday in Syria begin?

....

g Can you buy a cheap ticket to Sorrento after March 31st

....

h Where do you learn salsa dancing?

....

i What is the shortest time you can stay in Hong Kong?

....

j What's the price of the trip to Lille?

....

k Which holiday is cheaper for children?

....

l How many days does the tour of Syria last?

....

Ⓐ **Dance and ski in Spain**
Dance Holidays (01206-5777000) is offering a seven-day holiday combining skiing in the Sierra Nevada and salsa dancing in Granada. The price, £395, includes flights, <u>B&B</u> and ski pass.

Ⓑ **Eurostar to Lille**
Time Off (0870 584 6363) has two nights at the Grand Hotel Bellevue in Lille for £179. This price includes return Eurostar tickets, accommodation and breakfast.

Ⓒ *Bargain flights to Hong Kong*
Trailfinders (020 7938 3366) has cut-price fares to Hong Kong for only £310 on KLM. Departures are from Stansted Airport until 10 April. The minimum stay required is seven days, the maximum is one month.

Ⓓ *Bargain in Boston*
Virgin Holidays (01293 456789) has three nights at the two-star Midtown Hotel in Boston for £299 until 28 March. Flights depart from Gatwick and children under 11 pay half price.

Ⓔ *Tour of Syria*
The Imaginative Traveller (020 8742 8612) has a nine-day tour of Syria. The trip, which includes Palmyra and Damascus, leaves on 24 March and costs £695, with flights, hotels and guides.

Ⓕ *Week in Sorrento*
Citalia (020-8686 5533) has seven nights in Sorrento for £399. This includes <u>half-board</u> accommodation in the Hotel Bristol and flights. The offer applies to departures on 31 March.

<u>Glossary</u>   *B&B* = the hotel price includes bed and breakfast   *half-board* = the hotel price includes bed, breakfast and dinner.

Vocabulary booster: things you take on holiday

8 **a)** Dave is going on holiday. Look at the picture and tick (✓) the items in the box that he has remembered to pack. What has he forgotten? ....

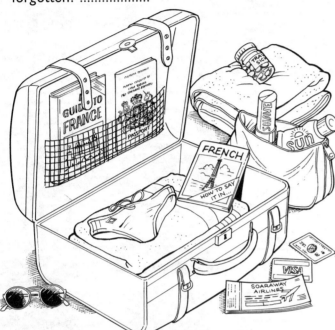

passport	sun cream	sunglasses	guide book
swimming trunks	shaving foam	phrase book
towels	credit cards	plane tickets	toothbrush
travel sickness pills

b) 📷 Listen to the pronunciation of the words. Practise saying them.

c) Put the words into one of the boxes below.

Things you need during a journey	Things you need for the beach	Things you need in a strange town	Other
passport	sun cream		

Improve your writing

More postcards

9 **a)** Read the three postcards below. In each case find:

1 Who sent the postcard, and from where.

   A ....

   B ....

   C ....

2 The relationship between the sender and the receiver.

   A ....

   B ....

   C ....

3 Is the sender enjoying her / himself?

   A ....   B ....   C ....

Ⓐ

Hi everyone!
I can't believe we're finally here-
it's fantastic, very hot and crowded (a bit like the office really..), lots to see and do; the food is really good (some dishes almost as hot as the weather!). Today we visited the famous Golden Temple and tomorrow we're going on an excursion to an island called Ko Sichang.
Don't work too hard! See you when we get back.
      Gill & Ruth
PS: Give our love to the big boss!!

Ⓑ

Dear Tanya,
Your father and I are spending a few days here at the seaside. The weather has been very wet so far, and unfortunately dad has got a bad cold so we can't go out; not much fresh air. We've seen some good programmes on TV, though. Hope you're enjoying yourself in London,
      Mum

Ⓒ

Dear Jo,
I'm sure you'll be surprised to get a card from me, but here I am! Last night we spent our first night out in the desert, and I must say it was fantastic. I never knew there were so many stars. And that it could be so quiet. I miss you, darling, and you know I'll be back one day. I just need some time, that's all. I hope you understand.
All my love,
      K. x

b) Write a postcard from one of the places on page 39 to either

- your teacher.
- someone in your class.
- someone in your family.
- a famous person.

Use some of the phrases from the box.

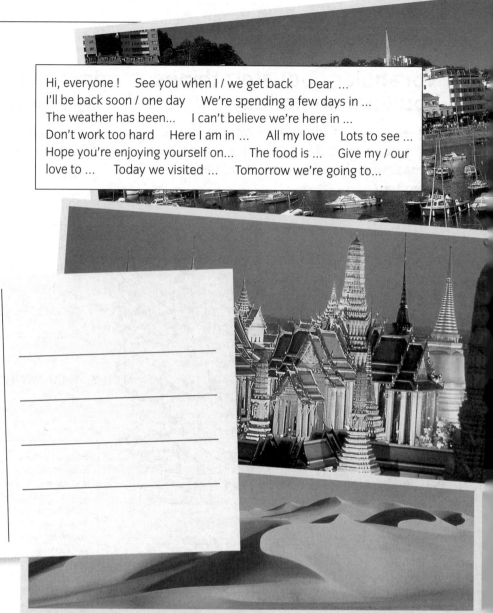

Hi, everyone !   See you when I / we get back   Dear ...
I'll be back soon / one day   We're spending a few days in ...
The weather has been...   I can't believe we're here in ...
Don't work too hard   Here I am in ...   All my love   Lots to see ...
Hope you're enjoying yourself on...   The food is ...   Give my / our
love to ...   Today we visited ...   Tomorrow we're going to...

Spelling

Words with -ed and -ing

10

> **LOOK!**
>
> Most of these words add -ing or -ed to the infinitive form.
> *interesting   interested*
>
> Words which end in -e **either**: drop the -e in the -ing form
> *come   coming*
> **or**: add -d in the -ed form
> *telephone   telephoned*
>
> Verbs which end in a consonant, a vowel and a consonant, double the final consonant in the -ing form.
> *put   putting*

How do you spell the -ing and -ed form of these verbs?

		-ing	-ed
a	climb	*climbing*	*climbed*
b	plan	....	....
c	disgust	....	....
d	surprise	....	....
e	relax	....	....
f	stay	....	....
g	cycle	....	....
h	move	....	....
i	enjoy	....	....
j	hope	....	....

module 7

Present Perfect

Positive, negative and question forms

1 Complete the gaps in the dialogues below with a word from the box. Use each word **twice**.

> 've   's   have   has
> haven't   hasn't

a A: I' (1) *ve*.............. just seen
a friend of mine on TV.
(2).................... you ever
appeared on television?
B: No, but my brother
(3).................... . He was in
a video a few years ago.
A: Really? Was it good?
B: I don't know.
I (4).................... seen it.

b My friend Florence
(5).................... always
wanted to be a successful
writer: she (6)....................
written four novels, but she
(7).................... made much
money.
I (8).................... read any of
them myself, but she tells me
they're very exciting.

c The Diamante Brothers
(9).................... been famous
for more than twenty years.
'A show business life is the
only life I (10)....................
known,' says Dion Diamante.
'It (11).................... been easy
for us to live a normal life.
But it (12).................... been a
fantastic life ... so far!'

Present Perfect and Past Simple with *for*

2 Underline the best tense, Present Perfect or the Past Simple.

a The Earth *existed* / *has existed* for more than 4,000 million years.

b Dinosaurs *have lived* / *lived* on Earth for 160 million years.

c Humans *have been* / *were* on the planet for just 50,000 years.

d For thousands of years, people *thought* / *have thought* that the world was flat.

e The first Australians – the Aborigines – *have lived* / *lived* there for about 40,000 years.

f People in Europe *have only known* / *only knew* about Australia for about 400 years.

g For many years, the United States *has been* / *was* a British colony.

h The USA *has been* / *was* an independent country for over 200 years.

i The dollar *has been* / *was* the currency of the United States for just over 200 years.

Present Perfect: short answers

> **LOOK!**
>
> **Short answers with the Present Perfect**
>
> Have I / you / we / they been to Japan?   Yes, I / you / we / they have.
> No, I / you / we / they haven't.
>
> Has he / she / it finished?   Yes, he / she / it has.
> No, he / she / it hasn't.

3 **a)** Read the results of the class survey and answer the questions. Use short answers.

	been to the USA?	passed driving test?	appeared on TV?
Rodolfo	✓	✓	✗
Hiroko	✗	✓	✗
Adam and Rachel	✓	✗	✓

1 Has Rodolfo been to the USA?   _No, he hasn't._

2 Has Hiroko passed her driving test?   _Yes, she has._

3 Has Rodolfo been to the USA?   ....

4 Has Rodolfo appeared on television?   ....

5 Has Hiroko been to the USA?   ....

6 Has Hiroko appeared on television?   ....

7 Have Adam and Rachel been to the USA?   ....

8 Have they passed their driving tests?   ....

9 Have they appeared on television?   ....

b) Answer these questions about yourself.

1 Have you seen a film this week?

....

2 Have you ever spoken to a famous person?

....

3 Have you made any phone calls today?

....

4 Have you heard of a singer called Sheryl Crow?

....

5 Have you made any mistakes in this exercise?

....

Present Perfect with *just*, *yet*, *already* and *never*

> **LOOK!**
>
> We often use *just*, *never* and *already* with the present perfect. These words come between *have* and the past participle.
>
> *They've **just** arrived.*
> *I've **already** done this exercise.*
> *I've **never** been to Australia.*
>
> *Yet* comes at the end of the sentence.
> *They haven't arrived **yet**.*

4 **a)** Put *just*, *already*, *yet* or *never* in the right place in the 'B' sentences

1 A: What's the difference between Great Britain and the UK?
   already
   B: I've told you twice!

2 A: Why are you looking so happy?
   B: I've heard that my cousin is coming to stay!!

3 A: Do you like Thai food?
   B: I don't know. I've tried it.

4 A: Is Ernesto here?
   B: No, he hasn't arrived.

5 A: Would you like to go and see *X-Men* tonight?
   B: Not really, I've seen it twice.

b) 📼 Listen to the answers on the tape. Practise saying the sentences.

Present Perfect and Past Simple with time phrases

5 In the sentences below, put the verb in brackets into the correct form: Present Perfect or Past Simple.

a   Carlos *visited*........................... (*visit*) the United States about twelve years ago.

b   .... (*go*) to the cinema lately? No, I .... (*not / have*) the time.

c   The plane .... (*take off*) at 8.15 … exactly on time.

d   I .... (*never / see*) anything so stupid in all my life!!

e   It .... (*be*) a bad day in the shop: so far this morning we .... (*not / have*) a single customer.

f   My parents .... (*get married*) when they .... (*be*) only nineteen years old.

g   I hope the weather gets better soon: it .... (*be*) really terrible this week.

h   Our son .... (*arrive*) in Australia three weeks ago, but he .... (*write*) to us yet.

i   Caroline .... (*go*) out a few minutes ago.

been or *gone*

> **LOOK!**
>
> *She's **gone** to school.*
>
> =
>
> She's at school, or on her way to school now.
>
> *She's **been** to school.*
>
> =
>
> She's not at school now.

6 Write *been* or *gone* in the following sentences.

a   'Where's Roberto?' 'He's *gone*............ home.'

b   I've .... to South America three times in my life.

c   'I'm sorry, you can't speak to Erik – he's .... out for lunch.'

d   I left my umbrella under the table half an hour ago, and now it's ....!

e   How many times have you .... to the supermarket this month?

f   He's nearly forty years old, and he's never .... abroad.

g   Anna was here a minute ago. Where's she ....?

Present Perfect and Past Simple

7 **a)** Complete this text about Cher, using the correct tense, Present Perfect or Past Simple.

Few stars (1) *have had* .... (*have*) careers as long and varied as Cher. In a career of more than three decades, she (2)........................... (*be*) successful both as a singer and as an actress.

Born Cherilyn Sarkasian LaPier in El Centro, California, on May 20th 1946, she (3)......................... (*leave*) home for Hollywood at the age of 16. When only seventeen she (4)......................... (*marry*) songwriter and record producer, Sonny Bono. As Sonny and Cher, they (5)......................... (*have*) several hits in the 60s, including 'I Got You Babe' in 1964. The couple's success (6)......................... (*continue*) with TV shows and a solo singing career for Cher. But in the 1970s, success (7)......................... (*be*) more difficult to find, and Cher and Bono (8)......................... (*get*) divorced in 1975. Soon after, Cher (9)......................... (*marry*) rock star Gregg Allman, but the marriage only (10)......................... (*last*) until 1979. She (11)......................... (*not / marry*) again. Since the mid-eighties, Cher (12)......................... (*have*) a second career – as an actress, appearing in films like *The Witches of Eastwick* and *Faithful*. In 1988, she (13)......................... (*win*) a Best Actress Oscar for the film *Moonstruck*. More recently, Cher (14)......................... (*return*) to singing once more, and with great success – her single 'Believe' (15)......................... (*become*) US Number One in March 1999.

b) 📼 Listen to the complete text.

Past Participles Wordsearch

8 **a)** There are 20 more irregular past participles in the box below. How many can you find? Write the past participle and the base form below.

1 *heard* .... *hear* ....
2 ....
3 ....
4 ....
5 ....
6 ....
7 ....
8 ....
9 ....
10 ....
11 ....
12 ....
13 ....
14 ....
15 ....
16 ....
17 ....
18 ....
19 ....
20 ....
21 ....

H	E	A	R	D	R	B	S	A	T	C
M	A	D	E	O	C	R	E	K	S	O
W	T	O	L	D	S	O	E	T	P	M
R	E	S	O	L	D	U	N	C	O	E
I	N	E	S	U	N	G	F	O	K	D
T	P	U	T	N	C	H	O	S	E	N
T	D	R	U	N	K	T	U	T	N	T
E	G	O	T	G	W	O	N	Y	C	S
N	D	F	Y	P	A	I	D	D	A	W

b) 📼 Listen to the pronunciation of the words on the tape. Practise saying them.

Vocabulary

Ambitions and dreams

9 Complete the phrases with the correct verbs.

a _go_........................... {
and live in the country
to university
abroad
}

b .... {
to speak a foreign language
to play an musical instrument
how to drive a car
}

c .... {
a degree
married
a job
}

d .... {
a millionaire
good at something
famous
}

e .... {
an interesting job
children
a large family
}

f .... {
a musical instrument
a sport
in a band
}

g .... {
a novel
a book
a poem
}

h .... {
a house
a car
your own home
}

Pronunciation

The sounds /æ/ and /ʌ/

10 **a)** 📼 We often pronounce the letter 'a' as /æ/. Listen to the example words. <u>Underline</u> the /æ/ sound.

married   family   language   Saturday

b) 📼 We often pronounce the letter 'u' as /ʌ/. Listen to the example words. <u>Underline</u> the /ʌ/ sound.

country   just   understand   money

c) 📼 Listen and write down the words you hear. Does each word have an /æ/ sound or an /ʌ/ sound?

1 _sat /æ/_........................
2 ....
3 ....
4 ....
5 ....
6 ....
7 ....
8 ....
9 ....
10 ....
11 ....
12 ....

d) Listen again and practise saying the words.

45

Improve your writing

A mini-biography

11 **a)** Read the text about jazz musician, Kenny G. Where should the five phrases below go in the text? Copy them in the correct space, as in the example.

A As well as making records,

B He was born in 1956 as Kenny Gorelick in Seattle, USA.

C During the last 20 years, Kenny has played with

D Kenny became well-known on the international music scene

E When he was just fifteen years old,

F ~~Saxophonist Kenny G.~~

Kenny G

The World's Favourite Jazz Musician ...

(1) _Saxophonist Kenny G_ . is now the world's most successful jazz musician. (2)...................... , and he learned to play the saxophone at an early age. (3)...................... , he toured Europe with his High School band. After studying at Washington University he started his career as a musician. In 1982 he signed for Arista records and made his first solo album _Kenny G_.

Success came slowly at first, but during the 1990s (4)...................... . He released _Breathless_, his most successful album so far in 1993, and in 1994 won the Best Artist award at the 21st American Music Awards held in Los Angeles.

(5)...................... he also found time to play in front of another famous saxophone player – US President Bill Clinton – at the 'Gala For The President' concert in Washington, and to break the world record for playing a single note (45 minutes and 47 seconds!) at the J & R Music World Store in New York in 1997.

(6)...................... superstars like Aretha Franklin, Michael Bolton and Whitney Houston and he has sold more than 36 million albums worldwide ... and he hasn't sung a note!

b) Write some sentences about a famous musician, actor or entertainer from your country. Use these phrases to help you.

> ... is ... (_country's_) most successful ...
> He was born in ... (_place_) in ... (_year_).
> After ... he started his career as a ...
> He became well-known during ...
> When he was ... years old, he ...
> During the last ... years he has ... and ... .

....
....
....
....
....
....
....
....
....
....

Kenny G

The World's Favourite Jazz Musician …

(1) *Saxophonist Kenny G* …… . is now the world's most successful jazz musician. (2)…………………… , and he learned to play the saxophone at an early age. (3)…………………… , he toured Europe with his High School band. After studying at Washington University he started his career as a musician. In 1982 he signed for Arista records and made his first solo album *Kenny G*.

Success came slowly at first, but during the 1990s (4)…………………… . He released *Breathless*, his most successful album so far in 1993, and in 1994 won the Best Artist award at the 21st American Music Awards held in Los Angeles.

(5)…………………… he also found time to play in front of another famous saxophone player – US President Bill Clinton – at the 'Gala For The President' concert in Washington, and to break the world record for playing a single note (45 minutes and 47 seconds!) at the J & R Music World Store in New York in 1997.

(6)…………………… superstars like Aretha Franklin, Michael Bolton and Whitney Houston and he has sold more than 36 million albums worldwide … and he hasn't sung a note!

Other phrases with and without *the*

6 Complete the sentences below with the correct preposition, with or without *the*.

a To make her apartment look more attractive, Tina decided to put some pictures *on the* wall.

b I don't want to go out tonight. I'd like stay .... home for a change.

c Because there are no buses, everybody had to go to work .... car.

d Marianne and her husband Tony first met when they were .... school.

e If you take your car to England, don't forget to drive .... left!

f There were no more chairs, so we had to sit .... floor.

g The quickest way to travel around Brazil is .... plane.

h August is a very quiet time in the city – most people are .... holiday.

i Of all the hotels .... centre of the city, I think The Metropole is the best.

j 'What do you study .... university?' 'Economics and English.'

k Walk along Main Street for 200 metres, and you'll see the railway station .... right.

l Here's my office telephone number if you want to ring me .... work.

Vocabulary
Geographical features

7 Choose a word from the box to complete the sentences.

> cathedrals   canals   volcanoes   the coast   deserts   scenery   ports   historical monuments   islands   the climate   ~~rivers~~

a Bridges go over them; fish live in them; they always go to the sea.
rivers

b Camels like them; they are very dry and often hot; you don't need an umbrella in them.
....

c It can be hot or cold, wet or dry, you can't change it!
....

d It's natural; people like looking at it; you see it in the countryside.
....

e People often go there for holidays; it's next to the sea; it can be rocky.
....

f They can be big or small; Ireland is one; they have water all around them.
....

g They can be dangerous; sometimes they get very hot; Sicily has a famous one.
....

h They're often near the sea or on a river; you see a lot of ships in them.
....

i They're religious buildings; you see them in cities; Paris has a famous one.
....

j They're usually straight; boats sail on them; Venice is famous for them.
....

k Tourists often visit them; they're always very old; and very beautiful.
....

49

Vocabulary booster: things you find in cities

8 **a)** Write the words for the pictures

a bridge	a fountain	skyscrapers	a statue
a mosque	a motorway	a market	a square
a church	a bus station	a park	an art gallery

1 *a statue*
2 ....
3 ....
4 ....
5 ....
6 ....
7 ....
8 ....
9 ....
10 ....
11 ....
12 ....

b) 📼 Listen and check. Practise saying the words.

c) Divide the words into four categories.

Buildings	Transport	Open Spaces	Other
a church	....	....	....
....	....	....	....
....			....
....			....

Spelling

Plural nouns

9 **a)** Look at these rules for the spelling of plural nouns.

> **LOOK!**
>
> Normally we form the plural of nouns by adding the letter -s.
> * Nouns ending in -s or -ss: add -es
>   gas   gas**es**
>   glass   glas**es**
> * Some nouns ending in -o: add -es
>   volcano   volcano**es**
> * Nouns ending in a consonant + -y: drop the -y and add -ies
>   lady   lad**ies**
> * Some nouns ending in -fe: changes to -ves in the plural
>   knife   kni**ves**
> * Some nouns are irregular:
>   child   child**ren**
>   foot   f**eet**

b) Write the plural forms of the nouns below.

1 kiss   *kisses*
2 potato   ....
3 baby   ....
4 woman   ....
5 watch   ....
6 man   ....
7 tomato   ....
8 tooth   ....
9 country   ....
10 life   ....
11 wife   ....
12 fly   ....

Listen and read

10 **a)** 🔊 Read and listen to the text about volcanoes.

escaping gases

lava

rock

We have all seen pictures like this from time to time ... perhaps you live in a country where there are volcanoes. Here are some of the most frequently asked questions about volcanoes.

▶ **What are volcanoes?**

A volcano is a mountain or hill with an opening through which steam, gases and lava from the centre of the Earth can escape into the air.

▶ **What is lava?**

Lava is red-hot rock which comes to the Earth's surface through the volcano. It has a temperature of about 1,000°C – ten times hotter than boiling water!! Lava can move as fast as 55 kph ... faster than most animals can run.

▶ **How many volcanoes are there in the world?**

There are about 850 active volcanoes in the world. About 60% are in an area called the Ring of Fire in the Pacific Ocean. The largest active volcano is Mauna Loa on the island of Hawaii.

▶ **What's the difference between 'active' and 'extinct' volcanoes?**

An active volcano can erupt at any time. Extinct volcanoes are volcanoes that have stopped erupting.

▶ **What happens when they erupt?**

A volcano erupts when there is a violent escape of gases and lava from the volcano. In 79 AD, Mount Vesuvius in Italy erupted, destroying the Roman city of Pompeii. The worst volcanic disaster in the 20th century was in Martinique, a French island in the Caribbean Sea. A volcano called Mount Pelée near the town of St Pierre erupted on the morning of May 8th 1902. Of the 30,000 people in St Pierre, just two survived.

▶ **Can we predict when a volcano is going to erupt?**

Nowadays, scientists usually know when a volcano is going to erupt. In 1991, the Pinatubo volcano,100 kilometres northwest of Manila in the Philippines, began one of the largest eruptions of the twentieth century. Thanks to the scientists' warnings, more than 100,000 people left the area before the volcano erupted on June 15th.

b) Complete the notes below with a name or number:

1   temperature of lava
    1,000°C ....

2   speed at which lava can move
    ....

3   number of active volcanoes in the world
    ....

4   percentage of volcanoes which are in the Ring of Fire
    ....

5   location of Mauna Loa
    ....

6   date when Mount Vesuvius erupted
    ....

7   location of Martinique
    ....

8   date when Mount Pelée erupted
    ....

9   number of people in St Pierre who died
    ....

10 number of people who survived
    ....

11 year when Pinatubo erupted
    ....

12 number of people who escaped
    ....

Improve your writing

Formal letters and informal notes

11 **a)** Colin has a Swiss-Italian friend, Antonella, and he wants to do an Italian language course this summer, either in Italy or in Switzerland. Read the advertisement below. <u>Underline</u> the course he should apply for.

Languages Live!!

Learn ■ English in England & the USA
■ Español en España, Mexico y Argentina
■ Français en France, Suisse et au Canada
■ Deutsch in Deutschland / Österreich / Schweiz
■ Italiano in Italia

Courses from 2 weeks to 9 months
All levels, all year round

Host Family Accommodation

For a **FREE** information pack please contact us at:

☎ Tel: **020 7753 2190** • Fax: **020 7753 9226**
e-mail: **langlive@ coserve.org.uk**
Website: **www.languageslive.co.uk**
Or write to: **Isabel McGowan, Languages Live!**
177 King Street, LONDON W1 6HH

---

b) Look at Colin's two letters on the right. One is a formal letter asking for information about Italian courses, the other is a note to his friend. Complete the two letters with words and phrases from the box.

15.11.01	Monday	the above address
Dear Ms McGowan	I'm sending you	~~16a~~
All my love	Just a quick note to say	Please send
I am interested in	I read	Yours sincerely	Colin
I'm sure I'll really enjoy reading it	Hi Antonella!!	

---

(1) _16a_. Berwick Street
Tiverton
Devon TI55 6FY

(2)...

(3)...

(4)... your advertisement in the *Education Gazette* of 15th November 2001. (5)... summer courses in Italian for summer 2002.
(6)... an information pack to me at (7)... . Could you please also tell me if you have any courses in Italian in Switzerland, and provide me with some information about what kind of accommodation you have available.
(8)..,

Colin Riley

Tiverton
(9) ....
(10) ....
(11) .... thanks for the book you sent me, which arrived yesterday.
(12) .... ! (But I'm going to need my Italian-English dictionary!!)
There's no real news here. I saw an advertisement for Italian courses in the newspaper today, so I've sent for an information pack.
(13) .... some more photos of our weekend in Newquay. You look great!!
Look after yourself,
(14) ....,
(15) ....

---

c) Either:

Write a letter similar to Colin's asking about courses in another language. Use your own name / address, etc.

or

Write Antonella's reply to Colin's note.

module 9

may, *might, will, definitely,* etc.

will / *won't*

1   **a)** On December 31st 1989, Madame Sol – a world famous astrologer – made some predictions for the 1990s. Write out the sentences using *will* / *won't*.

1   There / be / a woman President of the United States
   There will be a woman President of the United States.

2   People / not use / cash: / they / only use / credit cards

   ....

3   Astronauts / visit / the planet Mars

   ....

4   Great Britain / not have / a King or Queen

   ....

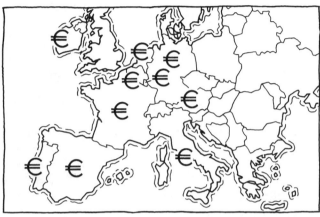

5   The countries of Western Europe / all use / the same currency

   ....

6   The millennium bug / destroy / the world's computers

   ....

b) Write some predictions of your own about the 21st century, using the ideas in the sentences.
   There won't be a woman President in my country in the next ten years.

may / might

2 Rewrite the following sentences using *may (not)* or *might (not)* instead of the phrase in **bold**.

a **It's possible that** Martin **will** be at Sally's party on Saturday.
Martin may/might be at Sally's party on Saturday.

b **Maybe** we **will** go abroad for our holidays next year.
....
....

c **Perhaps** they **won't** be able to finish the work until next week.
....
....

d You should take your coat; **it's possible that** it **will** get cold later.
....
....

e **Maybe** your mother **won't** want to go out this evening.
....
....

f **Perhaps** Martha **will not** be able to help you.
....
....

g **Maybe** the Prime Minister **will** resign if things don't get better soon.
....
....

h I always buy a lottery ticket: **it's possible that** I'll win £1 million one day!
....
....

will probably / probably won't

3 Doctors believe that about 355,500 babies were born all around the world on New Year's Day 2000. New Zealand had the first Millennium baby, a boy born at Waitakere Hospital in West Auckland at just one minute past midnight. What can we predict about his life in the third millennium? Complete each sentence with *will definitely / probably* or *definitely / probably won't*.

a He *will probably*........ have a completely normal life.
b He .... remember the Millennium celebrations.
c He .... be famous all his life.
d He .... be alive in the year 3,000.
e He .... see a lot of changes in the third millennium.
f He .... speak English when he's older.
g His parents .... become rich.
h People around the world .... forget about him in a few years.

will / won't / may / might

4 a) Read Sylvia Fox's daily horoscope on the next page. Which sign:

1 may have family problems this week?   *Cancer*..............
2 will have a good day at school?   ....
3 might need more money than usual this week? ....
4 will have more things to do than usual today? ....
5 may get very angry today?   ....

○ *Yesterday*

○ *Send this horoscope to a friend*

◉ *Tomorrow* ▶

Your Daily Horoscope for Wednesday May 17th by **_Sylvia Fox_**

Taurus

You might have an argument with an important person today. If this happens, you'll need help. A friend or partner will be very useful to you. And who knows ... you might win the argument!!

Gemini

This will be another busy work day for you: you'll have all the normal things to do, but there may also be an extra job or two. But don't worry, you'll succeed!! And think how happy you'll be when you finish!

Cancer

You may have to choose between your public and your private life today. You won't spend much time with your loved ones until later in the week. Make sure they know you love them, or they may feel forgotten.

Leo

This will be your lucky day for education! If you're still at school, it'll be a good day for study – something you've always thought was too hard for you will be easy. If you've already left school, think about going back to your studies – you won't regret it!

Virgo

There will be some money worries today. Check what you're spending – you may need to spend some extra money on travel, but if you buy something for a loved one, they may not thank you for it!!

b) <u>Underline</u> all the examples of predictions in the text.

c) 💻 Listen to some of the predictions on the tape.
· Practise saying the sentences.

Present tense after *if*, *when*, *before* and other time words

Present tense after *if*

5 Match the sentence halves and write out the complete sentence.

a *If the weather's good this weekend we'll have a barbecue in the garden.* ....

b ....

c ....

d ....

e ....

f ....

g ....

If the weather's good this weekend,	you'll pass all your exams.
If you work hard,	we'll be home before midnight.
If you're late for class again,	you'll get lost.
If you don't get up soon,	your teacher will get very annoyed.
If the train arrives on time,	we'll have a barbecue in the garden.
If you don't take a map,	we'll stop and have lunch.
If we see a restaurant,	you'll be late for class.

Time clauses: *if*, *when*, *before*, *as soon as*

6 <u>Underline</u> the best way to complete each sentence.

a I promise to telephone you *as soon as* / *before* / *if* I arrive.

b *As soon as* / *If* / *When* you don't leave me alone, I'll call the police!

c What are you going to do *as soon as* / *if* / *when* you finish university?

d If we drive quickly, we'll probably get home *before* / *if* / *when* it gets dark.

e This exam is very important for Margaret; *as soon as* / *if* / *when* she passes, she can go to university.

f 'Please check you have all your luggage *as soon as* / *if* / *when* you leave the train.'

g *As soon as* / *Before* / *If* you go, could you give me your e-mail address?

h Promise to tell me the news *as soon as* / *before* / *if* you hear anything.

i I'm sure I'll be married *as soon as* / *if* / *when* I'm 30.

Word order

7 Rearrange the phrases to make a sentence.

a   will - win - probably - I - Germany - think - the football match.
I think Germany will probably win the football match. ....

b   be - There - won't - any - tonight - snow - definitely

....

c   will - tomorrow - be - Stefan - definitely - at home

....

d   the answer - know - probably - to your question - won't - He

....

e   able - will - We - next week - be - to give - definitely - you - an answer

....

Vocabulary

Modern and traditional

8 a) Put the words in the box into one of the categories below.

fast food restaurant microwave mobile phone mall personal computer cassette player computer game electronic organiser photocopier e-mail hypermarket cooker compact disc (CD) letter address book diary fax corner shop

electronic goods	....
places to eat	*fast food restaurant*
places where you go shopping	....
things for cooking	....
things you can play	....
things you can send	....
things you write in	....

b) Complete the sentences with one of the words or phrases from the box.

1   It's quicker to cook food in a *microwave*.................. than in a normal oven.

2   Every day, Lucy writes about what happened in her ....

3   I write all my friends' phone numbers in my ....

4   Now there is a new .... near our home, we only do our food shopping every two weeks.

5   If you want to make some copies, you can use the office ....

Vocabulary booster: technology

9 **a)** Label the items in the shop window with a word from the box.

| answering machine   keyboard   laptop |
| computer   mouse mat   screen   fax machine |
| mouse   video recorder   printer |

b) 🖭 Listen to the pronunciation of the words. Practise saying them.

c) Which of the items:

do people often have at home?

....

can you carry around with you?

....

do people use at work?

....

....

....

Pronunciation

Different pronunciations of the letter 'i'

10 **a)** The letter 'i' can be pronounced

/ɪ/ as in *big*   /aɪ/ as in *microwave*

b) 🖭 How do we pronounce the *i* in these words? Listen and check. Write /ɪ/ or /aɪ/ for each word.

1 typewriter ..../aɪ/....
2 traditional ....
3 survive ....
4 public transport ....
5 definitely ....
6 bicycle ....
7 library ....
8 competition ....
9 mobile ....
10 equipment ....
11 might ....
12 deliver ....

c) 🖭 Practise saying the words, copying the voice on the tape.

module 10

Past Continuous

Important moments in history

1 Complete these sentences using the Past Continuous form of the verbs in brackets.

When SS Titanic hit the iceberg ...

a   people *were dancing* (*dance*) in the ballroom.

b   the captain .... (*read*) a book in his cabin.

When John Lennon met Paul McCartney ...

c   John .... (*play*) with a group called '*The Quarrymen*'.

d   rock 'n' roll music .... (*become*) popular in England.

When Neil Armstrong first walked on the Moon ...

e   the other astronauts .... (*sit*) inside Apollo 11.

f   millions of people .... (*watch*) it on television.

When Nelson Mandela left prison ...

g   his wife Winnie .... (*wait*) for him.

h   his supporters .... (*sing*) outside the prison.

Past Continuous and Past Simple

2 **a)** Put the verb in the correct tense, Past Continuous or Past Simple.

1   I .... (*watch*) TV at home, when someone .... (*come*) to the door.

2   My mother .... (*phone*) while I .... (*prepare*) dinner.

3   When we .... (*arrive*) home, some friends .... (*wait*) for us.

4   As I .... (*walk*) along the street, I .... (*see*) an old friend.

5   When I .... (*wake*) up, everyone .... (*look*) at me.

6   Jane .... (*see*) another guest who .... (*wear*) exactly the same hat!

b) 🔲 Listen to the sentences on the tape. Practise saying them.

59

3 Read the story of when Dave Mascott met his hero, and put the verb in brackets in the Past Simple or Past Continuous.

The famous American rock star Bob Goldhart (a) *was doing* .... (*do*) a tour of Britain when he (b) .... (*meet*) British rock star Dave Wells at a party. As he (c) .... (*leave*), Dave (d) .... (*invite*) Bob to come to his house and (e) .... (*tell*) him the address. But Bob (f) .... (*made*) a mistake as he (g) .... (*write*) down the address: he wrote 'Addison Street' instead of 'Addison Road.'

The next day, Helen Mascott of 145 Addison Street, London (h) .... (*listen*) to the radio in her kitchen when the doorbell (i) .... (*ring*). A man with long hair (j) .... (*stand*) outside. She (k) .... (*think*) the man (l) .... (*look*) familiar but (m) .... (*not say*) anything. 'Is Dave in?' the man (n) .... (*ask*) politely. The woman – whose husband's name was also Dave – (o) .... (*explain*) that Dave (p) .... (*do*) the shopping, but he would be back in a few minutes. She (q) .... (*invite*) Bob Goldhart to come in and wait. While Helen (r) .... (*make*) some coffee, he (s) .... (*look*) around the living room and (t) .... (*be*) very happy to see all of his albums!

A few minutes later, Dave (u) .... (*arrive*) home. 'You've got a visitor,' Helen (v) .... (*tell*) her husband. When Dave – a big, big fan of Bob Goldhart – (w) .... (*open*) the living room door and (x) .... (*see*) who (y) .... (*wait*) for him ... he (z) .... (*faint*)!!

used to / didn't use to

4 Roger Curry lives with his wife and three children in a castle in Scotland. He drives a Rolls Royce car, has a private plane and always wears expensive designer clothes. But things weren't always so good for Roger. Write three sentences with *used to* and one of the verbs in the box for each picture.

wear   have   be   work

a   *He used to have long hair.* .... (*long hair*)
b   .... (*moustache*)
c   .... (*old T-shirt*)

d   .... (*a very boring job*)
e   .... (*hamburger restaurant*)
f   .... (*poor*)

5 Write some negative sentences about Roger Curry using the words in brackets.

a (be / rich) *He didn't use to be rich.*

b (live / Scotland) ....

c (drive / Rolls Royce) ....

d (have / private plane) ....

e (wear / designer clothes) ....

Vocabulary

Accidents

6 Choose one of the verbs in the box to complete the sentences below.

| fall | ~~slip~~ | cut | touch | drop | bump | hurt |
| burn | break | bleed | | | | |

a As I was walking home one night, my foot *slipped* .... on some ice and I .... over.

b Be careful! There's some broken glass on the floor and I don't want you to .... yourself.

c Don't .... that electric wire ... you'll get a shock!

d After he .... his leg in a game, he never played football again.

e Sam had an accident while he was riding his bicycle: fortunately he didn't .... himself too badly.

f As the waiter was walking towards our table, he .... the plate he was carrying.

g Have you got a plaster? My finger's ....

h It was so dark when I walked into the room, I .... into a chair.

i Be careful when you use the iron: you might .... yourself.

Other health words

7 Read the clues and complete the words.

a A mark on your skin when you hurt yourself.
b r u i s e

b If you have this in your chest, it means that your chest hurts.
p _ _ _

c Doing this regularly helps you to stay healthy.
e _ _ _ _ _ _ _

d A piece of paper which means you can buy certain drugs.
p _ _ _ _ _ _ _ _ _ _ _

e You may need to drink this when you feel ill.
m _ _ _ _ _ _ _

f You may need one of these if you cut yourself.
p _ _ _ _ _ _

g The person you go to see when you're ill.
d _ _ _ _ _

h You need this if you're working hard!
r _ _ _

Articles

8 Complete the gaps with *a*, *the*, or – .

a What's *the* .... matter?
– I've got *a* .... headache.

b If you've got .... temperature, it's a good idea to stay in .... bed and keep warm.

c If you're taking .... prescription of .... antibiotics, you should always finish .... prescription.

d Is it OK to eat .... pasta if you want to lose weight?

e .... doctor says I should eat more .... fruit and .... vegetables.

f If you cut yourself on .... piece of broken glass, you should put .... plaster on it.

Listen and read

9 📟 Do you know the answers to these questions? Read and listen to the article *The Secrets of Sleep* and find the answers.

a How many hours a day do babies sleep?

....

b How many hours should we sleep?

....

c Give three reasons why it is bad for you to sleep for less than six hours a day.

....

d How many hours do most people sleep?

....

e Do older people need less sleep than younger people?

....

f Does sleeping more than ten hours help you to wake up early the next day?

....

The Secrets of Sleep

Babies do it for up to eighteen hours a day: **Mrs Thatcher and Napoleon both said they only needed to do it three or four hours a night. Sleep. No one can live without it. But how much do we really need?**

Research by the National Sleep Foundation in Washington says that we all need eight hours' sleep every night. Scientists have found that people who sleep for less than six and a half hours a night are more often ill than people who sleep for eight hours. Going without sleep also increases the chance of serious illness. 'Workaholics' who sleep for less than five hours often die young, and do less well at work.

The scientists found that, on average, adults sleep for seven hours a night, with 32% sleeping less than six hours.

It also says that the idea that we need less sleep as we get older is completely untrue. 'People have no idea how important sleep is to their lives,' Dr Thomas Roth, director of the Foundation says. 'Good health needs good sleep.'

'But not too much of it,' says Professor Jim Horne of Loughborough University. 'Sleep is like food and drink,' he believes: 'you would always like to have a little bit more, but that doesn't mean you need it.' Professor Horne studied a group of people who could spend as many hours as they wanted in bed; after ten hours they didn't find it any easier to get up in the morning. And people who sleep for more than nine hours a night die younger than people who usually sleep for seven or eight!

Adapted from The Week *4 April 1998 & 30 May 1998.*

Pronunciation

Different ways of saying the letter 'c'

10 **a)** How do we pronounce 'c' and 'ch' in these words?

> LOOK!
>
> Before *e* and *i* we usually pronounce *c* as /s/   *circle*
>
> Before *a*, *o* and *u* we usually pronounce *c* as /k/   *cough*
>
> We usually pronounce *ch* as /tʃ/   *chair*
>
> In some words we pronounce *ch* as /k/   *stomach*

medicine	/s/	headache	....	electricity	....
exercise	....	century	....	crash	....
backache	....	children	....	school	....
chest	....	cure	....	accident	....

b) 🔲 Listen and check. Practise saying the words.

Improve your writing

Adverbs

11 Choose an adverb from the box to complete each of the sentences below.

> suddenly   fortunately   eventually   immediately
>
> ~~unfortunately~~   certainly

a   Susan's grandmother really wanted to go to the wedding: *unfortunately* she was ill and couldn't go.

b   We waited nearly twenty minutes by the side of the road: .... a car stopped.

c   .... there was a loud noise and all the lights went out.

d   James was so tired when he got home that he went to bed ....

e   While she was riding home, Sophie fell off her bicycle: .... she wasn't badly hurt.

f   I don't know the exact age of this house, but it's .... more than one hundred years old.

module 11

Gerunds (-ing forms)

Expressing likes and dislikes

1 Use the prompts in box A and the sentence endings in box B to write sentences that are true for you.

A

look / after young children	walk / in the country
drive / very fast	sunbathe	work on a computer
swim / in the sea	jog	go / to the gym
travel / by plane	study / English	climb / mountains
drive / on the motorway	

B

... helps you to relax   ... is very boring
... makes you tired   ... is good for you
... is hard work   ... is good fun   ... is dangerous
... is bad for you

Looking after young children is good fun.
Looking after young children is hard work.

....
....
....
....
....
....
....
....
....
....
....
....
....
....

Gerunds after prepositions

2 a) Finish the second sentence so it has the same meaning as the first sentence.

1 Jack really loves surfing the Internet.
(*crazy about*)
Jack is crazy about surfing the Internet. ....

2 When I was young, collecting stamps interested me a lot. (*interested in*)
....

3 I'm very sorry: I just can't remember people's names! (*not good at*)
....

4 They left the restaurant; they didn't pay the bill. (*without*)
....

5 Why don't you do something and not just sit there? (*instead of*)
....

6 Does walking alone at night frighten you? (*frightened of*)
....

7 Katrina doesn't think about anything except making money. (*obsessed with*)
....

8 My father didn't have a problem with lending me the car. (*OK about*)
....

9 My sister loves shopping for clothes. (*mad about*)
....

b) 🔲 Listen to the sentences on the tape. Practise saying them.

Verbs of liking and disliking

3 The symbols on the table show what two children think of the things below. Write sentences to describe how they feel, using the phrases in the box.

really loves   doesn't mind   absolutely loathes
doesn't really like   really hates   is keen on
is not very keen on   really enjoys / likes
is crazy about   can't stand   likes

		Joseph	**Jessica**
a	maths	☺ ☺	☹ ☹
b	playing football	☺	☺
c	singing	☹ ☹	☺
d	reading	☺ ☺	☺ ☺
e	playing computer games	☺ ☺	☹
f	cooking	😐	☺ ☺
g	chocolate	☺	☺
h	doing homework	☹	😐

a   *Joseph really likes maths, but Jessica can't stand it.*

b   *They both like playing football. / They are both keen on playing football.*

c   ....

....

d   ....

....

e   ....

....

f   ....

....

g   ....

....

h   ....

....

Gerunds and infinitives

like doing and *would like to do*

4 **a)** Underline the best form: *like* or *would like* to complete the sentences below.

1   What do you think George *would like* / *likes* for his birthday this year?

2   Annette *likes* / *would like* Brad Pitt so much, she's got all his films on video.

3   Hello. *I'd like to speak* / *I like speaking* to Mr Shizuko, please.

4   *Would you like to go* / *Do you like going* for a coffee after class today?

5   One day, I *love going* / *would love to go* to Florida for a holiday.

6   Jenny always drives to college because *she doesn't like walking* / *she wouldn't like to walk.*

7   I *would love to be* / *love being* a professional ballet dancer, but I'm too tall.

8   It's late and *I'd like to go* / *I like going* home. Can you phone for a taxi?

b) 📼 Listen to the sentences on the tape. Practise saying them.

5 Read about Christopher Coleman. Correct the verbs in **bold** which should be in the *-ing* form.

Being
(a)**Be** addicted to something isn't so unusual; some people can't (b)**live** without (c)**smoke**; others enjoy (d)**shop**; there are plenty of people who say they are addicted to (e)**eat** chocolate; but Christopher Coleman, from Hampshire in the south of England, has a more unusual addiction.

'I've always loved (f)**drink** cola,' he said, 'but a few years ago I began (g)**buy** more and more. I couldn't (h)**sleep** at night, and I needed five cans in the morning to stop (i)**shake**!! In a normal day, I drank about forty cans. (j)**Get** enough cola every day was the only important thing in life!! It was terrible!! My girlfriend told me to stop (k)**spend** all my money on cola, but I didn't (l)**listen**. So in the end, she left me. 'That night I decided to give up (m)**drink** cola for ever'

me too / so do I etc.

6 a) Complete the gaps so that person B agrees with person A.

A

1 Mmm! I absolutely love strawberries!
2 I'm not very keen on driving.
3 Actually, I'm quite nervous about flying!
4 I felt really ill after that meal last night.
5 Yuk, I don't like this coffee!
6 Actually I'm a vegetarian now.
7 Bob was really angry after the meeting yesterday.
8 I didn't see the news last night.
9 I was a bit confused in that last English lesson.
10 Unfortunately I can't speak French.

B

Mmm. *So do I!* ....
Neither ....
Yes, me ....
So ....
Me ....
Really? .... I.
Yes, ... I!
Neither ....
Yes, me ....
Neither ....

b) 📼 Listen and repeat the responses.

Vocabulary booster: -ed and -ing adjectives

7 **a)** Match one of the adjectives with a face.

bored	interested	~~surprised~~	tired	relaxed
excited	frightened	worried		

5 ....

1 *surprised* ....

6 ....

2 ....

3 ....

7 ....

4 ....

8 ....

b) 🔊 Listen and check. Practise saying the words.

c) How do you feel when:

1 you listen to classical music?..............................
2 you watch a football match on TV? ....
3 you see a spider? ....
4 your best friend doesn't phone you for a few days?...
5 you stay up after 2 a.m.? ....
6 someone talks to you about cars? ....

> **LOOK!**
>
> Some adjectives have both -ed and -ing forms, for example: bored / boring.
> The -ing form describes the way something is.
> The -ed form describes the way it makes you feel.

d) Underline the best form, -ed or -ing.

1 Driving for a long time can be tired / <u>tiring</u>.
2 A long walk in the park can be relaxed / relaxing.
3 If you have nothing to do, you may be bored / boring.
4 A piece of news can be surprised / surprising.
5 You can be interested / interesting in football.
6 Going for a swim can be relaxed / relaxing.
7 A film can be excited / exciting.
8 People can be worried / worrying about losing their job.
9 Hard work can make you tired / tiring.

Spelling
Words ending with -ion

8 a) All these verbs have a noun form ending with -ion. Write the nouns.

1 collect   *collection*.......................
2 decide   ....
3 describe   ....
4 discuss   ....
5 educate   ....
6 explain   ....
7 invite   ....
8 permit   ....
9 prepare   ....
10 pronounce   ....

b) Complete these -ion words.

1 fa _ _ ion   6 rela _ ionship
2 ambi _ ion   7 tradi _ ional
3 obse _ _ ion   8 rev _ _ ion.
4 conversa _ ion   9 na _ ionality
5 profe _ _ ional

Pronunciation
Words ending with -ion

9 a) 🔊 Listen to the pronunciation of these -ion words. Is the -ion syllable strong or weak? Underline the stressed syllable in each word.

1 coll<u>ec</u>tion   7 permission
2 education   8 traditional
3 discussion   9 occasion
4 relationship   10 revision
5 decision   11 fashion
6 conversation   12 nationality

b) 🔊 Listen again and practise saying the words. Pay attention to the stress, and to the weak pronunciation of the -ion syllable.

Passive forms

Identifying Passive forms

1 Rock star Bob Goldhart has been one of the USA's favourite rock stars for more than 30 years. Here are the titles of some of his songs. Write **P** next to the song titles which include passive forms and **A** next to the songs which include active forms.

a 'When Will I be Forgiven?'   *P.*.........

b 'I was Made to Love You'   ....

c 'You Told Me You Loved Me (And That was a Lie)'   ....

d 'Rock 'n' Roll will Never Die'   ....

e 'My Heart was Stolen (By a Disco Queen)'   ....

f 'The Man who Bought the World'   ....

g 'My Heart is Made of Glass'   ....

h 'It Wasn't Easy (But I did it Anyway)'   ....

i 'Tonight Will Be the Most Beautiful Night'   ....

j 'I Am Adored (By all the World)'   ....

Present Simple Passive

2 Put the verb in brackets into the Present Simple Passive.

a About 300,000,000 photocopies *are made* .... (*make*) in Europe every day.

b The word *the* .... (*use*) 63,924 times in the Bible.

c 4,250 postmen .... (*bite*) by British dogs every year.

d 3,822 cars .... (*steal*) in the United States every day.

e 112 different languages .... (*speak*) in the Russian Federation.

f 71% of the world .... (*cover*) by water.

g In a normal year, five people .... (*kill*) by lightning in England and Wales.

h 2.4 litres of water .... (*lose*) by the human body every day.

Past Simple Passive

3 Complete the biography of the designer Gianni Versace by putting the verbs in brackets into the Past Simple tense.

Designer
of the Decade

Italian Gianni Versace was one of the best-known fashion designers of the twentieth century.

Sometimes his clothes (a) _were criticised_ (criticise), but they (b) .... (buy) by the rich and famous – particularly people from the worlds of pop music and film.

Versace came from Calabria, in the south of Italy, where his mother was a dressmaker. He moved to the northern city of Milan in the 1970s, and his first collection (c) .... (launch) in 1978.

Soon, his brother Santo and his sister Donatella (d) .... (give) jobs in the growing Versace Empire. He bought homes in Milan, Paris, New York and Miami, which (e) .... (fill) with works of art from all over the world.

In 1994, the English actress Elizabeth Hurley wore a Versace dress on the first night of the film *Four Weddings and a Funeral* in London. The simple black dress which (f) .... (hold) together by a few safety pins was a sensation. The next day, the photos (g) .... (see) all over the world and from that moment the name Versace (h) .... (know) everywhere.

His clothes (i) .... (wear) by superstars such as Elton John, Madonna, Courtney Love, Princess Diana and the supermodel Naomi Campbell.

Versace (j) .... (murder) on 15 July 1997 outside his home in Miami Beach. His memorial service in Milan Cathedral (k) .... (attend) by 2,000 people: millions watched on television as a tearful Elton John (l) .... (comfort) by Princess Diana – who herself died tragically just a few weeks later.

Future Simple Passive

4 In 1995, the World Economic Institute made some predictions for the 21st century. Complete them by putting the verb in brackets into the Future Simple Passive.

a   A new superhighway _will be built_ .... (build) which goes all the way from London to Beijing, in China.

b   Europe and Africa .... (join) by a tunnel at Gibraltar, off the south coast of Spain.

c   All the water problems of Africa .... (solve) by a new super lake.

d   90% of the world's business .... (do) on the Internet.

e   The world's weather .... (control) by satellites.

f   The Sahara and Arabian deserts .... (make) into agricultural areas.

g   Nuclear power .... (replace) by solar energy.

h   A world President .... (choose) by everyone who can vote.

Listen and read

5 **a)** 📼 Listen to and read the text *Diamonds are forever*.

Diamonds are forever

'Diamonds,' sang Marilyn Monroe in the film *Gentlemen Prefer Blondes*, 'are a girl's best friend.' You might not agree, but we can be sure of this: diamonds are not only the hardest substance in the world, they are also the most expensive. A single diamond cost $16.5 million when it was sold in Geneva in 1995!

Diamonds are found in a number of countries including Australia, South Africa, Brazil and The Russian Federation. In fact, there are two types of diamond; colourless diamonds (about 25% of those found) are the hardest and are often made into jewels. Black diamonds – the remaining 75% – are usually used by industry. Industrial diamonds are also produced artificially.

The largest diamond in history is the Cullinan diamond. It weighed 620g and was mined in South Africa in 1905. It was bought by the Transvaal Government for £150,000, and then it was presented to the King of England, Edward VII. The diamond was cut into smaller jewels, which are now part of the British Crown Jewels, which belong to the Queen of England and are kept in the Tower of London.

Diamonds are also used for decoration. Between 1885 and 1917, the Russian jeweller Peter Carl Fabergé made a number of decorated Easter eggs for the tsars and their families. The most valuable of them is decorated with more than 3,000 diamonds. It was sold at Christie's, Geneva, Switzerland for $5.5 million.

b) Using the information in the text, complete the sentences below with either the active or the passive form of the verb.

1 Marilyn Monroe / sing / *Diamonds are a Girl's Best Friend*

    Marilyn Monroe sang 'Diamonds are a Girl's
    Best Friend.'

2 A $16.5 million diamond / sell / in Geneva / in 1995

    ....

    ....

3 Diamonds / find / in many countries, including South Africa and The Russian Federation

    ....

    ....

4 Colourless diamonds / make / into jewels

    ....

5 Black diamonds / use / in industry

    ....

6 The Transvaal government / give / the Cullinan diamond to King Edward VII

    ....

    ....

7 The diamond / cut / into smaller diamonds

    ....

8 Peter Fabergé / make / egg which / sell / for $5.5 million at Christie's.

    ....

    ....

Active or Passive?

6 Tick (✓) the correct sentence.

1 a Twenty people arrested at the demonstration. ☐

   b Twenty people were arrested at the demonstration. ✓

2 a Mona Lisa painted Leonardo da Vinci. ☐

   b Mona Lisa was painted by Leonardo da Vinci. ☐

3 a Magellan sailed around the world about 500 years ago. ☐

   b Magellan was sailed around the world about 500 years ago. ☐

4 a Steven Spielberg directed the film *Schindler's List*. ☐

   b Steven Spielberg was directed the film *Schindler's List*. ☐

5 a *Romeo and Juliet* wrote William Shakespeare. ☐

   b *Romeo and Juliet* was written by William Shakespeare. ☐

6 a Unfortunately, our dog was killed in a road accident. ☐

   b Unfortunately, our dog killed in a road accident. ☐

7 a The cathedral in our town built about 400 years ago. ☐

   b The cathedral in our town was built about 400 years ago. ☐

8 a All her clothes are made in Italy. ☐

   b All her clothes made in Italy. ☐

Relative clauses with *which*, *who* and *that*

7 Cross out the incorrect words in the sentences below.

a a mobile phone *which* / ~~*who*~~ can send e-mails

b a computer *that* / *what* knows your voice

c the man *which* / *who* lives next door

d the girl *that* / *which* always sits next to me

e the bus *that* / *who* I take to get to school

f a meal *which* / *who* you can cook easily at home

8 Join each pair of sentences, using *which*, *that* or *who*.

a I've got a brother. He lives in Scotland

   I've got a brother who lives in Scotland.

b Henry's got a hat. It's red, green and blue.

   ....

   ....

c Claire is a writer. She is very famous.

   ....

   ....

d It's a salad. It tastes delicious.

   ....

   ....

e This is a picture. It was painted by Monet.

   ....

   ....

f He's a teacher. He is very popular.

   ....

   ....

g It's a machine. It makes pasta.

   ....

   ....

Vocabulary

Designer goods

9 Look at the words and phrases in **bold** on page 99 of the Students' book. Which word or phrase completes these sentences?

a A good pair of shoes will probably l *a s t* l *o n g e r* than a cheap pair.

b Many companies spend a lot of money on a _ _ _ _ _ _ _ _ _ _ so people know about their products.

c My nephew wants to buy a new jacket, but he'll have to s _ _ _ u _ f _ _ it.

d I always think it's a good idea to pay a bit more for things if they are b _ _ _ _ _ q _ _ _ _ _ _.

e It was so stupid of me to buy that designer dress: I look terrible in it. What a w _ _ _ _ o _ m _ _ _ _.

f Why should we s _ _ _ _ m _ _ _ _ o _ buying lunch when we can take sandwiches?

g In my opinion, the food you cook, is j _ _ _ a _ g _ _ _ as the food in an expensive restaurant.

h I'll have to buy a second-class ticket; the first class c _ _ _ _ f _ _ t _ _ much.

i That new computer is so expensive: I just c _ _ ' _ a _ _ _ _ _ it.

j One day, I'd love to o _ _ a really powerful car.

k Brown really isn't Liliane's best colour: I think she l _ _ b _ _ _ _ _ in black.

l A few books, some photographs and an old guitar were the only p _ _ _ _ _ _ _ _ _ _ he had.

Everyday objects

10 Here are some pictures of parts of some of the everyday objects on page 103 of the Students' book. Name the objects.

a *a corkscrew* ....

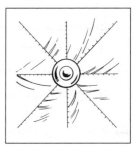

b ....

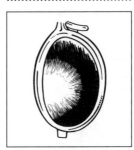

c ....

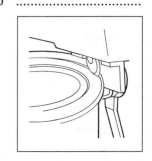

d ....

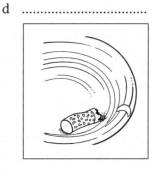

e ....

f ....

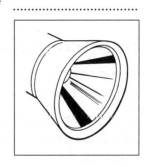

g ....

h ....

i ....

j ....

73

Spelling / Pronunciation

Silent 'g' and 'gh'

11 a) 📼 Listen to these words.

In the word *design*, the g is silent.
In the word *sunglasses*, it is pronounced as /g/.
In the word *night*, the gh is silent.
In the word *cough*, it is pronounced as /f/.

b) How are *g* and *gh* pronounced in these words?

Write *silent*, */g/* or */f/* by each word.

a li**gh**ter   *silent*
b lau**gh**   ....
c bri**gh**t   ....
d bou**gh**t   ....
e strai**gh**t   ....
f fri**gh**tened   ....
g si**g**n   ....
h enou**gh**   ....
i dis**g**usting   ....
j si**g**nature   ....
k hei**gh**t   ....
l green**g**rocer   ....

c) 📼 Listen and check your pronunciation. Practise saying the words.

Improve your writing

Joining sentences with *which*, *who*, *and*, *because* and *but*

12 a) Make one sentence from each pair of sentences using one of the words in brackets.

1 *What is it?*
   My best-ever present is a ring. I always wear on my left hand. (*which* / *what*)
   My best-ever present is a ring which I always wear on my left hand.

2 *Who gave it to you and when?*
   It was my grandfather. He gave it to me on my 18th birthday. (*who* / *which*)
   ....

3 *What does / did it look like?*
   It's made of gold. It has the letters H.M. on it. (*and* / *but*)
   ....

4 *More information*
   I always think of my family when I look at it. It used to belong to my great-grandfather. (*and* / *because*)
   ....

5 *Conclusion*
   I've had many presents since then. This has always been my favourite. (*and* / *but*)
   ....

b) Write a similar paragraph about your best-ever present. Use the questions to help you and try to use some of the linking words, *which*, *who*, *and*, *because* and *but*.

....
....
....
....
....
....
....
....
....
....
....

module 13

Present Perfect Continuous

1 Write one sentence using the Present Perfect Continuous for each pair of pictures.

a <u>*She has been working in the office for two hours.*</u> (*work*)

b .... (*rain*)

c .... (*play tennis*)

d .... (*walk*)

Time phrases with *for* and *since*

2 Write *for* or *since* next to these time phrases.

a *for*.................... a week
b *since*................ 1990
c .... twenty minutes
d .... he was born
e .... Thursday
f .... then
g .... last week
h .... 9 o'clock
i .... this morning
j .... you left school
k .... six months
l .... an hour
m .... twenty years

Present Perfect with *for* and *since*

3 Choose one of the phrases from Exercise 2 to complete each sentence in a logical way.

a Today's the last day of our holiday: we've been here *for a week*....................... .

b She left home two days ago, and no one has seen her ....

c You probably haven't studied mathematics ....

d I'm not surprised you're hungry – you haven't eaten ....

e The American singer Stevie Wonder has been blind ....

f Germany has been re-united ....

g Excuse me, waitress. Is our meal coming? We've been waiting .... !

h I've been driving .... and I've never had an accident!

4 Read the text and answer the questions below using the Present Perfect Continuous.

Success from abroad

Thomas Eckhardt: Thomas came to London from Germany almost four years ago. After doing a course in theatre costume design, he began working at the National Theatre in London a year ago. 'I really enjoy designing clothes, and I've always loved the theatre, so this job is absolutely perfect for me,' he says. 'I started work on a new production of *Romeo and Juliet* two weeks ago and I'm really excited about it.'

Bianca and Richard Jones: Bianca Jones is originally from Lima, in Peru. She came to England in 1997, and a year later she got married. For the last two years she has been manager of *La Finca* restaurant with her English husband, Richard. 'We were London's only Peruvian restaurant. It's been so successful that last week we opened a new restaurant – *La Finca II*.'

Florence Gauthier: Since coming to England almost twenty years ago as a language student, Florence has been a teacher – first of French at a secondary school, but now of yoga. 'I started studying yoga about ten years ago ... I enjoyed teaching French, but I wanted a change. I started teaching yoga about a year and a half ago, and I must say I really enjoy it.'

a How long has Thomas been living in England?
He *'s been living in England for nearly four years.*

b How long has he been working at the National Theatre?
He ....

c How long has he been working on *Romeo and Juliet*?
He ....

d How long has Bianca been living in England?
She ....

e How long has she been working at *La Finca*?
She ....

f How long has *La Finca II* been operating?
It ....

g How long has Florence been living in England?
She ....

h How long has she been studying yoga?
She ....

i How long has she been teaching yoga?
She ....

Present Perfect Simple or Continuous with stative verbs

5 Read the Look! box on page 24 of your Workbook again. The eight sentences below all use the Present Perfect Continuous. Four of them should be in the Present Perfect Simple. Find, underline and correct them.

a I've been working for about three hours. ✓

b I've been having this watch for over twenty years.

c The President has been talking for nearly an hour.

d How long have you been waiting?

e I've been liking chocolate for years.

f Have you been knowing Sylvia for a long time?

g She's been reading that book for weeks.

h I haven't been seeing Michael for years and years.

b - I've had this watch for over twenty years.
....
....
....
....
....
....

Vocabulary

Jobs and Personal Characteristics

6 Complete the gaps with a word from the *Jobs and Personal Characteristics* section on page 107 of the Students' Book.

a You need to be ...*careful*...... when you carry those glasses: they break easily.

b There are a number of people who are .... - .... for this job, so it's very difficult to choose the best one.

c It's very important to be .... when teaching someone to drive: don't get angry every time they make a mistake!

d We feel that Paul is too young for this job, and doesn't have enough ....

e One of the things people expect from a travel guide is a .... appearance.

f We can guarantee that you will learn English quickly at our school; we use all the ....

g I've always been .... , so I'm looking for a job in banking.

h When I explained to my boss why I was late, he was very .... and told me not to worry.

i In this job, we're looking for people with plenty of ideas; you need a lot of ....

j I'm sure nobody who works in this bar stole the money: I'm sure they're all completely ....

k We expect everyone who works in our shop to be .... - .... and to speak politely to the customers.

l She's an excellent travel agent; she's very .... , so all the customers like her.

Vocabulary booster: jobs

7 🔲 Match the jobs in the pictures to the words in the box. Then listen and check.

taxi driver   nurse   waiter   lorry driver police officer   pharmacist   shop assistant musician   tour guide   flight attendant

a ....

b ....

c ....

d ....

e ....

f ....

g ....

h ....

i ....

j ....

Reading

8 **a)** These job advertisements all come from the same Website: *Just Jobs*, which advertises jobs for young people all over the world. Read the advertisements and complete the table.

	the job	where it is	dates
1	....	....	....
2	....	....	....
3	....	....	....
4	....	....	....

Address: ▼ | www.jobsearch.com

jobsearch.com

Jobs for students, recent graduates and people looking for adventure

1

The Chaweng Beach Center, Samui
Management Trainee

Job Location: Samui Island, Suratthani, Thailand

Job Description: We are looking for an English-speaking person to work as a Management Trainee at the Chaweng Beach Center in Samui, Thailand. If you speak fluent English and want to work in the hotel and tourism business, why not apply for this job?

The working period will be from July to September 2001. Monthly salary of 6,000 baht; your accommodation and meals are free. Transportation and visa will be your responsibility. The hotel will arrange a work permit for you. For more information, please contact:

Training Manager.
The Chaweng Beach Center
63/3 Moo 5, Borpud,
Koh Samui, Chaweng Beach,
Suratthani, Thailand 82340
Phone: 66 77 231504
Fax: 66 77 231528
e-mail: chawenres@samart.co.th
www.centralbeachresorts.com

2

Hotel Waitress

Job Location: Island of Sark, Guernsey, Channel Islands

Region: UK

Job Description: Hotel Beauchamp, situated on the beautiful, small island of Sark in the Channel Islands, requires waitress from end of May until mid-September. 16-room private hotel with restaurant. Good salary and working conditions, live-in accommodation at the hotel. Experience not essential.

Contact: Mr & Mrs M. Robinson,

Hotel Beauchamp, Sark
Via Guernsey, Channel Islands GY9 OSF
Phone: 01481 238046
Fax: 01481 238469
e-mail: hotbe@island-of-sark.co.uk

next ▶

b) Now read the advertisements again and complete the table below.

	you need to ...	salary
1	*speak fluent English*	....
2	....	....
3	....	....
4	....	....

Back Forward Stop Refresh Home Favorites History Search AutoFill Larger Smaller Print Mail Preferences

Address: www.jobsearch.com

jobsearch.com

Jobs for students, recent graduates and people looking for adventure

3

Chamont Hot-Air Balloon Ground Crew

Job Location:	Europe
Region:	France, Switzerland, Austria, Italy
Job Description:	The Chamont Balloon Adventures team travels to France, Italy, Switzerland, Austria, the Czech Republic and Turkey, from May through October and the Swiss Alps, in January through February. Since 1977, we have offered hot-air balloon flights to an international clientele.
	To be a ground assistant, you must be fit, with a cheerful personality: Knowledge of spoken French, Italian and/or German is an advantage. Driving licence essential.
	Accommodation and food included, as well as a small salary. To apply send CV, ID photo and photocopy of driving licence.
	We are currently hiring for our summer season (24 May through 30 October).
Contact:	Michel Chamont
	Chamont Balloon Adventures Château de Labourde Dijon, FRANCE 21200 e-mail: mchamont@compuserve.com

4

Peking Garden

Chef - for Chinese takeaway

Job Location:	Tallinn, Estonia.
Job Description:	Qualified Chef needed for period of approximately six months in busy Chinese takeaway restaurant in Tallinn, Estonia. Salary $800-1000 per month. Please contact us by e-mail.
Contact:	Peking Garden Chinese Restaurant
	Pronksi 8-45 Tallinn, Estonia 10421 Phone: (372) 25023896 FAX: (372) 26184588 e-mail: peking@evr.ee

back

Pronunciation

Some 'hard to pronounce' words

9 **a)** Look at the words below. Is the sound in **bold** pronounced the same as the word in A or B?

	A	B
lawyer	how	✓ **four**
mayor	✓ **where**	higher
honest	not	home
patient	**pa**n	**pa**inting
psy**chia**trist	here	fire
awful	more	now
heal**th**	fell	feel
ar**chi**tect	**chi**ldren	headache

b) 📼 Listen and check. Practise saying both words, copying the voice on the tape.

Improve your writing

Error correction

10 **a)** Read the letter below. Find:

1 three punctuation mistakes (full stops, capital letters etc.)

2 three layout mistakes (where things are on the page)

3 four spelling mistakes

4 two mistakes of politeness

b) Write out the letter in full, correcting all the mistakes.

374 Upper Road
Islington
London
N1 2XG

Tel. 020 7359 1410

May 26th 2001

hello Sir!

    I am writeing to apply for a job as a member of your hot air balloon ground crew. I inclose a CV, ID photo and photocopy of my driving licence as requested. I am avalable to start work immediatly.

Thanks a lot

Jean Guinard.

DRIVING LICENCE
1. GUINARD
2. JEAN

UK

3. 05-07-83 UNITED KING
4a. 16-03-99   4b. 03-03-0

5. GU
7.

8. 374 UPPER ROAD, IS
LONDON N1 2XG

9. B, B1, f,k,l,n

Curriculum Vitae

Jean

Michael Chamont
Chamont Balloon Adventures
Château de Labourde
Dijon
FRANCE 21200

module 14

some, any and quantifiers

some, any and no

1 Complete the sentences with *some*, *any* or *no*.

a Helga can't work abroad because she doesn't speak ...*any*............... foreign languages.

b Would you like .... more coffee before you leave?

c There are .... letters for you over there, on the table.

d Do you have .... questions you'd like to ask me?

e If there are .... more questions, we can finish now.

f I'm afraid there's .... ice cream in the fridge. How about .... fruit instead?

g Can you buy .... bread when you go to the supermarket?

h I can't get a ticket from the machine – I haven't got .... change.

i There are .... food shops open in the village on a Sunday, so you'll have to eat in a restaurant.

much, many, a lot of, a few, no

2 a) Look at the picture of Luke's bedroom. Complete the sentences about Luke using the words in the box.

much	many	a lot of	a few	no	a

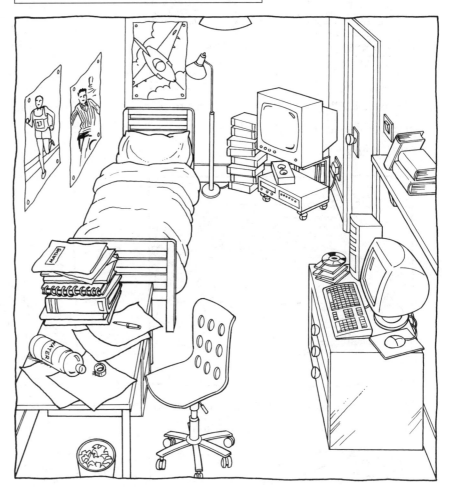

1 There isn't ..*much*............ space in his bedroom.

2 He hasn't got .... books.

3 He's got .... work to do!

4 He's got .... videos.

5 There are .... pictures on the wall.

6 There is .... water in the bottle.

7 He's got .... computer, and .... computer games.

8 There are .... plants in his room.

b) 📼 Listen and check your answers. Practise saying the sentences.

too and *not ... enough*

3 Complete the sentences in two ways using *too* or *not ... enough* using the adjectives in brackets.

a My sister is 12 years old. She can't get married because she *isn't old enough. / is too young.* .
(*old / young*)

b We couldn't swim in the sea because the water
.... (*cold / warm*)

c They can't all travel together because the car
.... (*big / small*)

d Margaret sold her old computer because it
.... (*fast / slow*)

e The child couldn't reach the sweets because the shelf .... (*high / low*)

f I don't think Dan will be a successful basketball player because he
.... (*small / tall*)

Prepositions

Describing where things are

4 There are fifteen Easter eggs in the picture. Where are they?
Write a sentence to describe the position of each egg, using
a word from the box.

> above   next to   in the corner   behind (x 2)   opposite   near
> between   at the bottom of   inside (x 2)   in front of   under
> outside   on top of

a   *There's an egg above the mirror.* ....

b   ....

c   ....

d   ....

e   ....

f   ....

g   ....

h   ....

i   ....

j   ....

k   ....

l   ....

m   ....

n   ....

o   ....

Vocabulary

Adjectives for describing places

5 Cross out the adjective which does **not** go with the noun.

a	A(n)	quiet	attractive	elegant	~~slow~~	**street.**
b	A	private	large	wooden	sunny	**garden.**
c	A(n)	modern	spacious	attractive	private	**kitchen.**
d	A(n)	old-fashioned	private	wooden	elegant	**table.**
e	A(n)	colourful	elegant	simple	quiet	**dress.**
f	A	dark	simple	large	lovely	**meal.**
g	A(n)	three-storey	old-fashioned	dark	attractive	**room.**

Prepositions

6 Complete each sentence with *in*, *at* or *on*.

a She owns a very comfortable apartment .*in*.................. the suburbs.

b Their office is .... the sixth floor.

c How many times must I tell you not to leave your clothes .... the floor!

d There's a small shop .... the end of the road.

e My office is .... the city centre.

f When my parents retired, they went to live .... a small village.

g Our family owns a holiday home .... the coast.

h Lydia's family were waiting for her .... the garden.

Describing houses and apartments

7 The answers to the questions come from the *Describing houses and apartments* section in the Students' Book on page 118.

a Which **A B** is a building where lots of people live?
A *partment*........ B *lock*.............. .

b Which **B** is a place outside a room where you can sit and look out?
B ....

c Which **B** is a general word for houses, offices, etc.?
B ....

d Which **C** is an open space in the middle of a large building?
C ....

e Which **F** is a general word for chairs, tables, beds, etc?
F ....

f Which **F** is where you make a fire to heat a room?
F ....

g Which **F** is what you stand (or sit!) on in a room?
F ....

h Which **K** is the place where you do your cooking?
K ....

i Which **L R** is the room where you sit and read or watch TV?
L .... R ....

j Which **P** is something you can walk along in a garden or park?
P ....

k Which **R** is something you use to decorate the floor?
R ....

l Which **S** is an area where people live outside the city centre?
S ....

m Which **V** is smaller than a town or city?
V ....

Vocabulary booster: things in a house

8 **a)** Find these things in the picture and write the correct letter in the box next to the word.

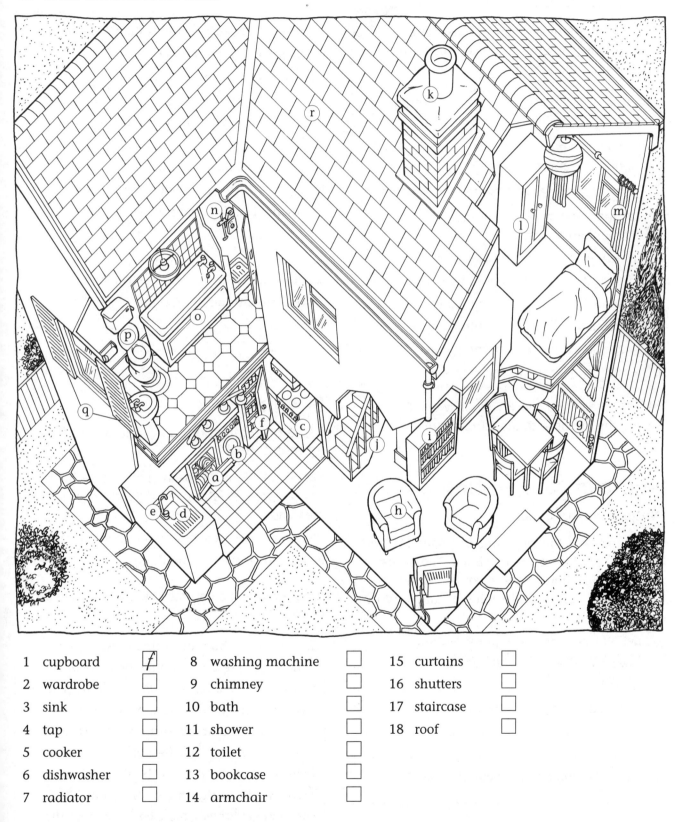

1	cupboard	f	8	washing machine	☐	15 curtains ☐
2	wardrobe	☐	9	chimney	☐	16 shutters ☐
3	sink	☐	10	bath	☐	17 staircase ☐
4	tap	☐	11	shower	☐	18 roof ☐
5	cooker	☐	12	toilet	☐	
6	dishwasher	☐	13	bookcase	☐	
7	radiator	☐	14	armchair	☐	

b) 📼 Listen to the pronunciation of the words. Practise saying them. As you say them, point to the item in the picture.

Pronunciation

Compounds with two nouns

> **LOOK!**
>
> In English, there are many nouns made of two words (compound nouns). Notice the stress on the first word:
>
> | | | | |
> |---|---|---|---|
> | noun + noun: | bath + room | ⇨ | bàthroom |
> | -ing form + noun: | dining + room | ⇨ | dìning room |

9 a) Mark the stress on these compound nouns.

1	armchair	7	dishwasher
2	courtyard	8	apartment block
3	fireplace	9	living room
4	bedroom	10	washing machine
5	bookcase	11	swimming pool
6	tennis court	12	building site

b) 📼 Listen and check your answers. Practise saying the nouns with the correct stress.

Improve your writing

Notes giving directions

10 Look at the directions on pages 119 and 120 of the Students' Book. The notes below explain how to get to some holiday apartments from St Christopher's Station. Write full sentences.

a get off train / St Christopher's Station
Get off the train at St Christopher's Station.

b come out of station / turn left
....
....

c walk / Station Road / about fifty metres
....
....

d there / bus stop / on / right. Take / number 11 / to Sandy Bay
....
....

e get off / see large petrol station / on corner / take / about ten minutes
....
....

f cross road / walk about 100 metres
....
....

g take / first turning / left, where / see sign saying 'Holiday Apartments'
....
....

h down hill towards sea / see 'Holiday Apartments' office on right- / open 9–5
....
....

Spelling

Same pronunciation, different spelling (homophones)

11 a) Many words in English have the same pronunciation, but different spelling and meaning:

There were **two** people sitting in the square.

It was **too** dark to see anything.

b) Underline the correct spelling of each word in the text below.

> If you need to buy something to eat, there's a [1]knew / <u>new</u> restaurant quite near [2]hear / here which you could try: we [3]ate / eight there last week and had a very good meal. When you come out of the house, turn [4]right / write. Walk along the [5]road / rode for about a hundred metres, [6]passed / past the bank, and you'll [7]sea / see the restaurant on the corner. Make sure you get [8]their / there early, because the restaurant always gets very full [9]buy / by about [10]ate / eight o'clock.

module 15

Past Perfect

1 a) Put the verbs in brackets into the Past Perfect to complete the sentences below.

1 Nadia said she was very sorry for what she
   had done .... (do).

2 When Sam
   .... (pay)
   the bill, we left the restaurant and went home.

3 It wasn't surprising that she was tired: she
   ....
   (not / sleep) for two days.

4 The children were very excited because they
   ....
   (not / see) a tiger before.

5 The road was blocked because a lorry
   ....
   (break down).

6 During the afternoon, David lost all the money he
   .... (win)
   in the morning.

7 My mother felt very nervous on the plane because she
   ....
   (not / fly) before.

8 When the police arrived to arrest him, Thompson
   ....
   (leave).

b) 📼 Listen to the sentences and practise saying them.

Past Perfect and Past Simple

2 Complete the text about Arthur Ferguson, using the verbs in the box.

| died | had arrested | was | had emigrated | wasn't | didn't know |
| had bought | had | sent | found | had sold | had tried |

When, in 1926, a US court (a) _sent_ .... a man called Arthur Ferguson to prison for five years, it (b) .... the end of an amazing criminal career. The police (c) .... him several months earlier, when he was trying to sell the Statue of Liberty to an Australian tourist. After the arrest, the police soon (d) .... that it (e) .... the first time that Ferguson (f) .... to make money by selling famous buildings.

Ferguson (g) .... to the United States from Scotland the previous year. Soon after his arrival, he found a luxurious house in Washington for a rich Texas farmer; but the farmer (h) .... that he (i) .... the White House, home of the Presidents of the United States for hundreds of years!

Before coming to America, Ferguson (j) .... Buckingham Palace – home of the English royal family – for £2,000, Big Ben for £1,000 and Nelson's Column for £6,000 – all to rich American tourists who perhaps (k) .... more money than intelligence!

When Ferguson (l) .... , in 1938, he was a rich man.

Reported speech

Direct to reported speech

3 Here are some of the things Arthur Ferguson said to the man who nearly bought the White House. Put them into reported speech.

a 'It's one of the most beautiful houses in Washington.'
He said (that) it was one of the most beautiful houses in Washington.

b 'The house belonged to my grandfather.'

....

c 'My grandfather died last month.'

....

d 'I don't want to sell the house, but I can't afford to keep it.'

....

e 'You and your family will be very happy here, Mr Taylor.'

....

f 'The house is worth $100,000 but I'll sell it to you for $50,000.'

....

Reported to direct speech

4 The police arrested a man for the theft of a painting from The Denton Art Gallery. He said that he was innocent. Write the suspect's original words.

a The suspect said his name was Ricky Davies.
'My name is Ricky Davies.'

b He told the police that he lived with his mother at 43, Fountain Road, Denton.

'...

....'

c He said that he had spent the evening watching *The Lion King* at the ABC Cinema.

'...

....'

d He said that he'd fallen asleep during the film, so he couldn't remember the story.

'...

....'

e He said that the film had finished at about 10.30.

'...

....'

f He said that after the film, he had taken a number 85 bus home to Fountain Road

'...

....'

g He said that he had gone to bed at 12 o'clock, after his mum had read him a story.

'...

....'

Prepositions

5 Complete the gaps with the correct preposition.

a I tried to borrow some money *from*............. my parents, but they said no.

b When I have enough money .... the bank, I'll retire.

c Thomas spends about £150 a month .... clothes.

d Can I change this money .... US dollars, please?

e The government should invest more money .... the transport system.

f I'm afraid you can't pay .... credit card in this restaurant: they only accept cash.

g 'How would you like to pay, madam?' 'I'll pay .... cash.'

Irregular Past forms

6 Underline the correct form of the verb to complete the sentences.

a The show had already *began* / *begun* when we got to the stadium.

b It was a marvellous show, and Maria *sang* / *sung* beautifully.

c I was very tired because I had *drove* / *driven* all the way from Edinburgh to London.

d While I was swimming in the sea, someone *stolen* / *stole* my clothes.

e When she died in 1999, the novelist Iris Murdoch had *wrote* / *written* twenty-seven novels.

f The X-rays showed that Laurence had *broke* / *broken* his leg.

g I had never *saw* / *seen* anything so beautiful in my whole life.

Vocabulary

Verb phrases to do with money

7 Make a sentence in column B which has the same meaning as the sentence in column A.

A

1 The computer was too expensive for me to buy.

2 Philip borrowed £1,000 from his friend Gill.

3 In this job, your salary will be £30,000 a year.

4 I borrowed £10 from Joseph, and I haven't paid it back yet.

5 I was very disappointed by the holiday. I feel that I spent my money stupidly.

6 In the TV Programme *Millionaire* you can receive up to £1 million by answering simple questions.

7 Instead of eating in restaurants, I'm going to eat at home to spend less money.

8 Jimmy put $100,000 on Japan to win the World Cup.

9 The government wants to give more money to the car industry.

10 When the company closed, all the investors' money disappeared.

B

1 I *couldn't afford*.............. the computer.

2 Gill .... £1,000 to her friend ....

3 In this job, you will .... £30,000 a year.

4 I .... Joseph £10.

5 I was very disappointed by the holiday. I feel that I .... my money.

6 In the TV Programme *Millionaire* you can .... up to £1 million by answering simple questions.

7 Instead of eating in restaurants, I'm going to eat at home to .... money.

8 Jimmy .... $100,000 that Japan would win the World Cup.

9 The government wants to .... more money in the car industry.

10 When the company closed, the investors .... all their money.

Listen and read

8 **a)** Complete the text using the phrases in the box.

> But they weren't used in Europe   a thing of the past   ~~How much money~~
> began to appear   a £10 bank note   about 2,700 years ago
> pieces of paper   as people became rich

1 *How much money* .... have you got with you today? How many coins? How many notes? Why is money so important anyway? If you think about it, coins are just discs of metal, and bank notes are just 2.. . Money is only money if we agree that it's worth something! Nowadays, governments print bank notes and guarantee their value. As well as the Queen's head, all British bank notes carry the words: *I promise to pay the bearer on demand the sum of ...* That means that – in theory – it's possible for you to take 3.. to the Bank of England and ask for £10 of gold in return. We don't suggest you try it, though! The United States government, for example, stopped exchanging bills for gold in 1971.

Over the years, money has taken many forms: in China people used precious shells; hundreds of years later the Vikings in Northern Europe used jewellery, and the people of ancient Tibet once used blocks of dried tea! People from ancient Lydia (Turkey) were the first to make coins, 4.. . The coins were made from electrum, a mixture of gold and silver. It wasn't until the 11th century that paper bank notes 5.. in China. 6.. until the Middle Ages when traders and bankers used 'bills of exchange' instead of cash. The modern industries of banking and insurance soon followed 7.. through trade between East and West.

With the growth of the 'virtual economy', some people predict that, by the end of this century, coins and notes will be 8.. : we will all use 'smart cards' to buy things. No more worries about losing your wallet or purse ... but what if you lose the card??

b) 📼 Listen and check your answers.

c) Answer the questions below about the text.

1 Can you really change a £10 note for £10 of gold at the Bank of England?
....

2 Can you exchange dollar bills for gold in the USA?
....

3 What did people use for money in
a) Ancient China? ....
b) Viking Europe? ....
c) Ancient Tibet? ....

4 Who made the first coins? When?
....
....

5 When did the first bank notes appear? Where?
....
....

6 When did bank notes first appear in Europe?
....

7 What do some people predict will replace money?
....

Pronunciation

The sounds /eɪ/ and /e/

9 **a)** 🔊 Listen to the /eɪ/ and /e/ sounds in the following words.

/e/	/eɪ/
lend	break
bread	day
spend	make

b) Look at the sentences below. Mark the /eɪ/ and /e/ sounds.

1 I've made about ten phone calls today.
   /eɪ/   /e/   /eɪ/

2 They wasted all the money we gave them.

....

3 You said you'd never played tennis until today!

....

4 Have you read the book I lent you, by the way?

....

5 She said she'd pay me back at the end of April.

....

6 Jane made a terrible mistake.

....

c) 🔊 Listen and check your answers. Practise saying the sentences

say or *tell*

10 Complete each sentence with *say*, *tell*, *said* or *told*.

a What does that sign .say.............? Can you read it from here?

b I saw Donna today and she .... me you were engaged. Congratulations!

c John just stood there and .... nothing.

d Why didn't you .... me that you'd be late?

e The Prime Minister appeared on TV and .... that the government would spend more money on education.

f I wanted to .... something, but I decided it was better to wait.

g I phoned my friend and .... her that I'd be a few minutes late.

h .... me what happened.

Improve your writing

Punctuation in direct speech

11 **a)** Read the text below and look at the notes.

> One day, the British Education Minister Stephen Byers was visiting a school. He said how important it was for children to learn mathematics at an early age.
> '[1]What are eight sevens?[2]' a journalist asked.
> '[1]I was worried you would ask me that[3]' replied Mr Byers[3], '[1]I think it is 54'.[4]

1 ' ' These are *inverted commas*. They come before and after the speaker's original words.
2 ? A *question mark* comes after a question in direct speech. It comes before the second *inverted commas*.
3 Look at this final sentence. There is a *comma* at the end of the speaker's words, before the second *inverted comma*. Then there is another *comma* before the first *inverted comma* when the speaker's words start again.
4 At the end of the sentence, the *full stop* (.) comes after the *inverted commas*.

b) Now put the correct punctuation in the sentences below.

1 'Has your mother arrived yet?' asked Clara.
2 I didn't play very well today Peter Salmon said but I still think I can win tomorrow.
3 Where are you going the policeofficer asked us.
4 Two coffees please I said to the waiter and can we have the bill please.
5 Are you ready yet shouted Neil's mother I'm waiting.
6 I've bought you a present said Christine I hope you like it.

module 16

would and *wouldn't*

1 Complete the sentences with *would* or *wouldn't*.

a I like working: if I didn't have a job, I *would* soon get bored.

b I'm very happy in the city: I .... enjoy living in the country – it's too quiet!

c My sister is very honest: if she found some money in the street, I'm sure she .... take it to the police.

d I .... like to be famous: I'm quite happy as I am!

e Nobody has read the fire instructions: if there were a fire, they .... know what to do.

f We can't go to Asia by bus: the journey .... take much too long.

g If I could live my life again, I .... change anything.

Second Conditional

2 Put the verbs in brackets into the correct tense to make conditional sentences.

a I'm sorry, I don't know. If I *knew* .... (know) the answer, I *would tell* .... (tell) you.

b If I .... (not / work), we .... (not / have) enough money to live.

c I'm sure you .... (feel) better if you .... (not / get up) so late.

d If you .... (can) meet a famous person from history, who .... (like) to talk to?

e I don't know what I .... (do) if you .... (be / not) here to help me.

f If I .... (have) a lot of money, I .... (take) you on an expensive holiday.

g If everyone .... (speak) the same language, do you think life .... (be) better?

h If you .... (have) twenty brothers and sisters, think how many birthday presents you .... (get)!

might or *would* in Second Conditional sentences

3 a) Match the sentence halves.

1 He might help you

2 She wouldn't go out with him

3 If I could go on holiday anywhere in the world,

4 Robert might do better at school

5 If you told her the truth,

6 If you didn't drink so much coffee before going to bed,

a I'd go to Florida.

b if you were more polite to him.

c you might sleep better.

d if he didn't have so much money.

e if he did his homework regularly.

f she might get very angry.

b) 📼 Listen to the sentences on the tape. Practise saying them.

First and Second Conditional forms

4 Tick (✓) the correct sentence for each situation below.

1 Someone asks you to help them to translate a newspaper article into your language. Unfortunately, the newspaper article is in Chinese – a language you don't speak or understand.
What do you say?
a *I'll help you if I can.*
b *I'd help if I could.* ✓

2 Someone asks about your plans for tomorrow. You're not sure yet – you're either going to the beach or to the cinema – it depends on the weather.
What do you say?
a *If the weather's good, I'll go to the beach.*
b *If the weather was good, I'd go to the beach.*

3 You're on holiday at the seaside. The beach is very nice, but unfortunately the weather isn't very good – it's cloudy and the temperature is only 12°C. Someone asks if you're enjoying yourself.
What do you say?
a *I'd be happier if the weather was better.*
b *I'll be happier if we have better weather.*

4 You invite a friend to go to a club with you, but she's got an exam tomorrow, so she can't come. What does she say to you?
a *I'll come if I don't have an exam.*
b *I'd come if I didn't have an exam.*

5 A taxi driver is driving you very slowly to the station. Your train leaves in five minutes. What do you say to him?
a *If we don't go faster, I'll miss the train.*
b *If we didn't go faster, I'd miss the train.*

6 A friend asks you to drive her home from a party, but your car is at home, so you can't help her.
What do you say?
a *Sorry, if I have my car, I'll take you home.*
b *Sorry, if I had my car, I'd take you home.*

7 You see a child crossing the road reading a book. What do you say to the child?
a *If you're not careful, you'll have an accident.*
b *If you weren't careful, you'd have an accident.*

will or would

5 Underline the best form in each sentence, as in the example.

a I _wouldn't_ / _won't_ do that if I were you!

b Goodbye, everybody! _I'd_ / _I'll_ see you all next week.

c _I'd_ / _I'll_ help you if I had more time.

d What time _will_ / _would_ you be back from work this evening?

e I _won't_ / _wouldn't_ be surprised if they won the competition.

f Sorry, I can't speak now. _I'd_ / _I'll_ phone you back later.

g _I'll_ / _I'd_ be here until 6 o'clock if you need anything.

h Life _will_ / _would_ be so much easier if people worked together.

i If my mother were here, I'm sure _she'd_ / _she'll_ know what to do.

Short answers with _will_ and _would_

> **Will** you / he / she / it / we be at home? Yes, I / he / she / it / we **will**. No, I / he / she / it / we **won't**.
>
> **Would** you / he / she / it / we work ? Yes, I / he / she / it / we **would**. No, I / he / she / it / we **wouldn't**.

LOOK!

6 Write short answers to these questions.

a Would you travel to another planet if you had the opportunity?
Yes, I would....

b Will your brother be at home if I phone this evening?
No, ...

c Would you like to be Prime Minister of your country?
No, ...

d Will we have time for lunch when we get there?
Yes, ...

e If you won the lottery, would you give up work?
Yes, ...

f Would you move to a bigger house if you had the money?
No, ...

g If Kate and Roger get married, do you think they'll be happy?
Yes, ...

h If a stranger offered you £1,000 to carry a bag onto an aeroplane, would you do it?
No, ...

Vocabulary

Wordbuilding

7 Complete the gaps with the correct form of the word in brackets.

a The President of the United States is perhaps the most _powerful_ person in the world. (_power_)

b John Lennon died .... in December 1980. (_tragedy_)

c It's a lovely hotel: very quiet, and in the middle of really .... countryside. (_peace_)

d There was a .... smell of cigarettes in the room. (_strength_)

e The police were worried that the demonstration might become .... (_violence_)

f In this zoo, the animals can move around .... (_freedom_)

Vocabulary booster: people in politics, religion and public life

8 **a)** Put the people in the box into the word map.

the Prime Minister   a communist   a Catholic   a Mayor   the President
a priest   the Vice President   a Queen   a Buddhist   a social democrat
a King   a Muslim   a Member of Parliament   a judge   a Protestant
a government minister   a Christian   a Hindu   a green

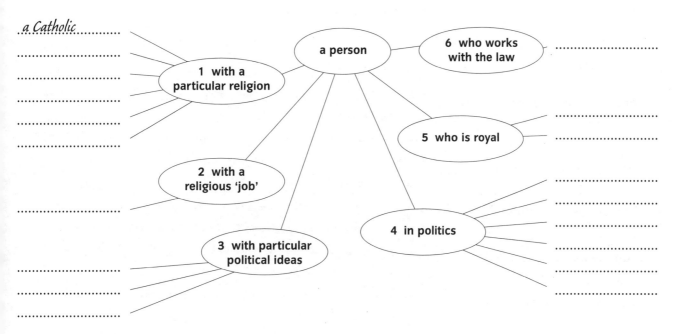

a Catholic

a person

1 with a particular religion

6 who works with the law

5 who is royal

2 with a religious 'job'

4 in politics

3 with particular political ideas

b) 📼 Listen and practise the pronunciation of the words.

c) 📼 <u>Underline</u> the correct answer in the general knowledge quiz below.
Listen and check your answers.

1 Mecca is a very important city for *Hindus / Muslims.*

2 Lenin was a *communist / social democrat* leader.

3 Rome is the centre of the *Protestant / Catholic* church.

4 Margaret Thatcher was the first woman *Prime Minister / President* of the United Kingdom.

5 The Netherlands has *a President / a Queen.*

6 The British Chancellor of the Exchequer is *a government minister / a kind of priest.*

7 Most people in India are *Hindus / Buddhists.*

8 George Bush Senior was *the President / the Prime Minister* of the United States.

Spelling

Silent 'w'

9 a) Sometimes the letter 'w' is silent. Which of the 'w's below are silent?

would	~~wrong~~	whole
weight	when	walk
answer	why	songwriter
whose	worried	wrote

b) 🔊 Listen and cross out the silent 'w's.

c) Complete the rules below with examples from part a.

1 If a word begins with **wr**, 'w' is always silent, for example ....

2 If a word begins with **who**, 'w' is usually silent, for example ....

3 A few other words have a silent 'w', for example ....

Pronunciation

The sound /w/

10 🔊 Listen and practise the /w/ pronunciation in these words and phrases from module 16.

will	won't
words	wouldn't
world	war
whites	wife
to win	an award
to wonder	working

Improve your writing

Error correction

11 Here is a student's letter for the Writing activity on page 137 of the Students' book. The teacher has marked 22 mistakes, using the following code:

Sp for a spelling mistake

P for a punctuation mistake

WW for a wrong word.

Write the corrections below.

Planet Hero

Hello everybody!

Here we are! We've finally arrived and I'm ¹writeing [Sp] to you from the Planet Hero!

There's enough oxygen and lots of plants, but ²fortunately [WW] the weather isn't very good and ³its [P] rained every day so far – as you can see it isn't all that ⁴diferent [Sp] from life in ⁵england [P]!

The journey was very, very long – ten weeks on a spaceship – ⁶then [WW] it was quite ⁷boreing [Sp] at times. I read all the books ⁸what [WW] you gave me during the first week, ⁹but [WW] I had to watch Space TV instead.

The other six people here are all very nice: one of them is a ¹⁰docter [Sp] from ¹¹france [P] – his ¹²names [P] ¹³rené [P].

Today we met our first Herovian (¹⁴thats [P] the name for the people ¹⁵which [WW] live here) and guess what? He speaks ¹⁶english [P]!

This morning I saw a small green person ¹⁷siting [Sp] on a wall, looking at me.

'Hello,' I ¹⁸sayed [Sp], 'what's your name ¹⁹. [P]

²⁰Fine [P], thanks, he answered and ran away.

Anyway, it's ²¹geting [Sp] late, so I'd better go to bed. Give my love to all my ²²frends [Sp] and family.

Simona

1	9	17 ....
2	10	18 ....
3	11	19 ....
4	12	20 ....
5	13	21 ....
6	14	22 ....
7	15	
8	16	

Answer key

Introduction

Grammar terms

1

b	possessive adjective	h	noun (countable)
c	pronoun	i	article (definite)
d	modal verb	j	noun (uncountable)
e	adverb	k	preposition
f	auxiliary verb	l	article (indefinite)
g	main verb		

2

b	sweet	g	fun, love
c	a (secret)	h	want, see, love, stop
d	a secret	i	can, might
e	me, you	j	your, my
f	never, always		

module 1

Question forms
Word order

1 a)

2 Is your family here with you?
3 Does your wife enjoy athletics?
4 Do you like life here in Italy?
5 Are you worried about the Italian champion, Giacomo Zanetti?
6 Do you have any advice for young athletes?

Question words

2

b	Which	e	When
c	Where	f	Who
d	What	g	How many
		h	How
		i	How long
		j	Why

Subject and object questions

3

b	won	e	do you already know
c	do you want	f	told
d	knows	g	do you live
		h	lives
		i	smokes
		j	broke

Present Simple

4 b)

2 They don't live in the same country: they live in different countries.
3 She doesn't live in the United States, she lives in London.
4 She doesn't work in the evening, she works in the morning.
5 She doesn't play golf, she plays tennis.
6 She doesn't stay in a hotel, she stays with her sister.
7 They don't see each other every weekend, they see each other two or three times a year.

c)

2 What time does she get up?
3 What time does she finish work?
4 Where does Rosemary Wilson live?
5 How often does she come to England?
6 Why does she come to England?
7 Who does she stay with? / Where does she stay?

Short answers

5 c)

1	No, they don't.	3	Yes, they do.
2	No, they don't.	4	Yes, they do.

Frequency
Phrases

7

b	three times a year	e	four times a week
c	once a week	f	twice a day
d	twice a year	g	once a month

Vocabulary booster: sports

8 a)

2	cycling	6	horse riding	10	gymnastics
3	skiing	7	table tennis	11	volleyball
4	swimming	8	basketball		
5	ice-skating	9	boxing		

c)

2 baseball, table tennis, basketball, volleyball
3 skiing, swimming, ice-skating
4 horse riding, cycling
5 gymnastics, boxing

Vocabulary
Phrases with *go* and *play*

9

go	go to the	play	play the
shopping	gym	chess	guitar
skiing	cinema	football	violin
ice-skating	park	table tennis	trumpet
dancing	beach	computer games	piano

Pronunciation
The /ə/ sound

10 a)

1	nev·er /ə/	5	en·ter·tain /ə/	9	pop·u·lar /ə/
2	am·bi·tion /ə/	6	pro·fes·sion·al /ə/ /ə/ /ə/	10	pre·sent·er /ə/
3	com·put·er /ə/ /ə/	7	lei·sure /ə/		
4	ex·er·cise /ə/	8	foot·bal·ler /ə/		

Improve your writing
Punctuation (1)

11 'Everybody thinks I'm a typical Englishwoman,' actress Kate Thomson told *Go!* magazine. 'I really don't know why ... '. When she was 18, Kate left England. She lived first in Canada, then Morocco, where she met French film producer Serge Roux. The couple now live in Paris with their three children: Patrick, James and Lucie. 'We're so happy here. It's nice to have children who can speak both English and French.'

module 2

Past Simple
Regular and irregular verbs

1

appear – appeared	buy – bought	cost – cost
drive – drove	fall – fell	find – found
go – went	know – knew	look – looked
make – made	play – played	take – took
begin – began	come – came	die – died
eat – ate	feel – felt	get – got
happen – happened	live – lived	lose – lost
meet – met	read – read	write – wrote

2

b was	g met	l got	q wrote		
c began	h fell	m had	r looked		
d played	i was	n cost	s read		
e went	j knew	o made			
f died	k found	p was			

Negatives and affirmatives

3

b It didn't begin in October 1936, it began in October 1946.
c It wasn't about a rich farmer who moved to New York, it was about a rich woman who moved to the country.
d The woman didn't fall in love with her cousin, she fell in love with a handsome young farmer.
e Her lover wasn't married to her cousin, he was engaged to her cousin.
f The producers of the programme didn't have a lot of money, they had very little money.
g The assistants didn't write the words on pieces of paper, they wrote them on blackboards.

did, *was* or *were* in questions and answers

4

2 was	7 did	12 didn't	17 did
3 did	8 were	13 wasn't	18 was
4 Was	9 Were	14 didn't	19 did
5 wasn't	10 was	15 was	20 did
6 was	11 weren't	16 Did	

Time phrases often used in the past
in, at, on

6

b at, c –, d at, e on, f at, g in, h in

Vocabulary
Words to describe feelings

7

b fed up	f guilty	j frightened
c excited	g in a good mood	k embarrassed
d relaxed	h bored	l angry
e disappointed	i surprised	m nervous

Listen and read

8 **a)**

1 – a, 2 – a, 3 – b, 4 – c, 5 – c,
6 – b, 7 – c, 8 – c, 9 – c, 10 – b

Spelling
-ed endings

9 **b)**

1 believed	4 dropped	7 married	10 studied
2 cried	5 hurried	8 phoned	11 tried
3 continued	6 used	9 stopped	12 danced

Pronunciation
-ed endings

10

2 listened (2)	6 used (1)	10 stayed (1)
3 wanted (2)	7 loved (1)	11 acted (2)
4 compared (2)	8 hated (2)	12 enjoyed (2)
5 tried (1)	9 remembered (3)	

Linkers: *but, so, because, then*

11

b because	d then	f but	h because
c so	e but	g so	i then

module 3

can / can't

1 **a)**

2 My sister can speak three languages perfectly.
3 I'm sorry, you can't bring your dog in here.
4 Nowadays, you can buy cheap aeroplane tickets on the Internet.
5 Bad news: Renate can't come to the party on Saturday.
6 Can you read Russian? I don't understand this.
7 'I'm sorry we can't answer the phone at the moment: please leave a message ...'
8 'Can we have a table by the window?'

can / can't / have to / don't have to

3

b Can	g Can	l Can
c can't	h can't	m have to
d don't have to	i have to	n can't
e have to	j has to	
f can	k can	

should / shouldn't

4

NB: Some answers may be different in different cultures!

b	should	e	shouldn't	h	should
c	shouldn't	f	shouldn't		
d	shouldn't	g	should		

Short answers with modal verbs *can*, *should*, *have to*

5 **b)**

2	No, you don't.	5	Yes, you should.	8	Yes, I can.
3	Yes, we should.	6	Yes, you do.		
4	Yes, you can.	7	No, I don't.		

Prepositions

6

b of, c out, d to, e down, f for, g at, h in, i on, j to

Vocabulary booster: things in a school

7 **a)**

1	video recorder	8	rubber
2	whiteboard	9	cassette player
3	pencil case	10	ruler
4	overhead projector	11	pencil sharpener
5	bookcase	12	notebook
6	hole punch	13	file
7	board rubber	14	waste bin

c)

Uses electricity	Doesn't use electricity – usually metal	Doesn't use electricity – not metal
cassette player	hole punch	rubber
overhead projector	pencil sharpener	bookcase
video recorder	waste bin	ruler
	file	whiteboard
		board rubber
		notebook
		pencil case

Vocabulary

Wordbuilding

8 **a)**

improvement	interruption	explanation
imagination	practice	
advice	pronunciation	

b)

impróvement	interrúption	explanátion
imaginátion	práctice	
advíce	pronunciátion	

c)

2	communication	5	interruptions	8	explanation
3	imagination	6	practice		
4	advice	7	pronunciation		

Collocations

9

b	work	h	read
c	get	i	listen
d	make	j	forget
e	understand	k	praise
f	have	l	become

Pronunciation

How to pronounce the letter 'a'

10 **b)**

/æ/ e.g.: *have to*
have to
practise
exam
Spanish
understand

/ɑː/ e.g.: *can't*
can't
mark
hard
far

/eɪ/ e.g.: *make*
make
communicate
take
game
mistake
education

Improve your writing

Writing a paragraph

11 **1)**

The best order is:

1 c   2 a   3 d   4 b

2)

a	paragraph c	c	paragraph d
b	paragraph a	d	paragraph b

Spelling

Finding mistakes

12 **a)**

Stefanie is very pleased – she has won a competition at her college. The prize is a two-month language course in Edinburgh. She will have English lessons for three hours every morning, but she wants to know the best way to improve her English outside her lessons.
Her friends, family and teachers have lots of advice!

module 4

Present Continuous

1

b am I driving? / you are
c are you doing? / I'm not watching
d I'm looking for / Are you sitting
e isn't working / is spending

Present Simple or Present Continuous?

2

b are you doing
c you're listening to
d are you reading
e Do you smoke
f are you laughing
g Does your brother play
h Are you listening

State and action verbs

3

3 I'm not believing you! ✗
   I don't believe you!
4 Do you want a drink? ✔
5 I'm not understanding him. ✗
   I don't understand him.
6 I'm hating cold weather! ✗
   I hate cold weather.
7 I don't understand Turkish. ✔
8 I'm not knowing her name. ✗
   I don't know her name.

Present Continuous for future arrangements

4

Example sentences
Steve isn't working on Monday.
He is going to Manchester for the day on Tuesday.
He is taking/catching the train at 6.45.
Judy is working on Monday, Tuesday and Wednesday.
She is meeting Alison for lunch (at 1 o'clock on Friday).
Steve and Judy are going to the cinema on Thursday.
Steve's mum is coming to babysit.
Oliver is playing football on Tuesday at 4 o'clock.
He is going to Tom's house after school on Wednesday.
Florence is going swimming on Monday.
Oliver and Florence are meeting their cousins in the park at 2.30 on Friday.
The whole family is going to the grandparents' house for lunch on Sunday at 12 o'clock.

Vocabulary booster: special occasions

5 a)

1 cards
2 decorations
3 the host and hostess
4 guests
5 glasses
6 sandwiches
7 presents
8 someone making a wish
9 candles
10 birthday cake
11 paper plates
12 paper cups

Vocabulary
Things people do on special occasions

6

b send
c stay
d visit, give
e go
f have
g buy
h make
i have
j have
k spend

Listen and read

7 a)

1 Diwali
2 Easter in Poland
3 Ramadan
4 Easter in Poland
5 Ramadan
6 Diwali
7 Diwali

b)

1 No
2 The ninth month of the Islamic calendar.
3 coloured eggs, bread, salt and white sausages.
4 breakfast
5 India
6 five days
7 Laxmi

Improve your writing
A letter of invitation

8

10 Fife road
Norton

October 7th

Dear Tony,

Sorry I haven't written for so long, but I've been really busy with the new job. I hope you're well and still enjoying life at university.

The main reason I'm writing is to tell you that Valerie and I are staying at Uncle Frank's villa in Spain for the Easter holidays. Would you like to come and stay for a few days? The villa is in a really beautiful place, very near the beach. You can fly to Malaga airport and get a bus from there.

Can you give me a ring to tell me if you're interested? Our new phone number is 01804 742 3812. We'd love to see you!

See you soon,
mark

Spelling
-ing forms

9

celebrating	getting ✓	living	taking ✓
cooking ✓	giving	putting ✓	wearing
driving	inviting	studying ✓	writing

Pronunciation
/ð/ and /θ/

10 a)

/ð/	/θ/
Mo<u>th</u>er's Day	bir<u>th</u>day
Fa<u>th</u>er's Day	twenty-fif<u>th</u>
<u>th</u>e o<u>th</u>er day	four<u>th</u>
<u>th</u>e day before yesterday	<u>th</u>irty-first
<u>th</u>ese days	your good heal<u>th</u>
in <u>th</u>ose days	<u>Th</u>anks for coming!

module 5

Comparatives and superlatives
Comparative forms

1 a)

2 younger – Paul is younger than Mike.
3 taller – Paul is taller than Mike.
4 faster – Paul is faster than Mike.
5 more experienced – Mike is more experienced than Paul.
6 slower – Mike is slower than Paul.
7 heavier – Mike is heavier than Paul.
8 more aggressive – Mike is more aggressive than Paul.
9 more powerful – Mike is more powerful than Paul.
10 more popular – Paul is more popular than Mike.

Superlative forms

2

a oldest
b fastest / quickest
c richest / wealthiest
d most popular / most important
e shortest / longest

3

b 'The reason I wanted to be an actress was to play people much <u>more interesting</u> than I am, and to say things much <u>more intelligent</u> than anything I could think of myself.'
c 'All animals are equal, but some are <u>more equal</u> than others.'
d 'Good, <u>better</u>, <u>the best</u>
Never let it rest
Until good is <u>better</u>
And <u>better</u> is <u>the best</u>'
e It was <u>the best</u> of times, it was <u>the worst</u> of times.
f Being funny is much <u>more difficult</u> than being clever.

Prepositions in comparative phrases: *as, than, from, like, in, to*

4

b	as	d	than	f	in	h	like
c	than	e	like	g	from		

Describing what people look like
Questions about appearance

5

b What does she look like?
c How tall is she?
d Is she black or white?
e What's her hair like?
f What colour are her eyes?

is or *has got*?

6

a 's got / 's got / hasn't got
b are / are / 've got
c is / 's got
d 's got / hasn't got
e 's / 's.

Vocabulary
Describing appearances

7

1				W	I	G			
2		A	T	H	L	E	T	I	C
3		B	R	A	V	E			
4	S	U	N	T	A	N			
5		W	H	I	T	E			
6	D	R	E	S	S	E	D		
7		S	H	I	N	Y			
8		N	E	C	K				
9		P	A	L	E				
10		S	L	I	M				
11		M	A	K	E	U	P		
12		P	E	R	F	U	M	E	
			?						

look

8

2	-looking	5	Look!	8	look out of
3	have a look	6	look like	9	look up
4	look for	7	looking forward to	10	look at

Vocabulary booster: parts of the face and body

9 a)

1	head	6	chest	11	hair	16	face
2	shoulder	7	fingers	12	nose	17	teeth
3	arm	8	leg	13	mouth	18	neck
4	hand	9	feet	14	eye		
5	back	10	toes	15	ear		

c)

1	head, neck, face, mouth, nose, back, chest
2	ear, eye, leg, hand, feet, arm, shoulders
10	fingers, toes
32	teeth
Uncountable!:	hair

Improve your writing
Writing a description

10 a)

2 – A, 3 – C, 4 – B, 5 – D, 6 – F

Pronunciation
Different ways of pronouncing the letter 'o'

11

3	different	6	the same	9	the same
4	the same	7	different	10	the same
5	different	8	different		

Spelling
Double letters

12

The incorrectly spelt words are:
slimmer, pretty, different, biggest, attractive, middle-aged, well-dressed, glasses, tanned, appearance.

module 6

Intentions and wishes
going to and planning to

1

b Lucy says she's going to spend the summer with her family.
c John and his wife aren't planning to have any more children.
d Caroline is planning to look for a job after she finishes her exams.
e Which film are you going to see this evening?
f Is it true that the President is planning to retire soon?
g Is the school going to organise a barbecue this Sunday?

going to, planning to, would like to, would prefer to

2

b	prefer to	e	planning to	h	is going
c	not planning	f	to retire	i	I would
d	He's	g	I'm planning		

Predictions
will and won't

3

b Do you think we'll be able to buy tickets when we get there?
c I'm sorry, but there won't be any time for us to have lunch.
d Will you be all right if I go out for a couple of hours?
e I'm going to Michelle's party on Sunday. Will you be there too?
f Don't worry. I'm sure there won't be any problems getting a visa.
g How long will it take for us to get there?
h Will there be any food at your party?

Short answers with will, won't and going to

4

b	No, I'm not.	f	Yes, I am.	j	No, it isn't.
c	Yes, it is	g	No, it won't.	k	No, they won't.
d	No, I won't.	h	Yes, I / we will.		
e	No, they're not.	i	No, he isn't.		

Pronunciation
'll, will and won't

5 b)

2	We'll	5	Will she	8	She won't
3	Will you	6	she won't		
4	I will	7	They'll		

Vocabulary
Holidays

6 a)

2	luxurious	7	polluted	12	crowded
3	boiling	8	windy	13	peaceful
4	disgusting	9	tasty	14	sandy
5	lively	10	terrible	15	wet
6	relaxing	11	fantastic		

b)

2	tasty	7	lively	12	luxurious
3	popular	8	boiling	13	sandy
4	wet	9	relaxing	14	terrible
5	windy	10	polluted	15	disgusting
6	crowded	11	peaceful		

Listen and read

7

a Lille, b 020 7938 3366, c seven nights,
d the Midtown Hotel, e £395, f 24th March, g no,
h in Granada (Spain), i seven days, j £179,
k Bargain in Boston, l nine

Vocabulary booster: things you take on holiday

8 a)
He has forgotten his toothbrush.

c)

Things you need during a journey	passport, plane tickets, travel sickness pills
Things you need for the beach	sun cream, sunglasses, swimming trunks, towels
Things you need in a strange town	guide book, phrase book, credit cards
Other	shaving foam, toothbrush

Improve your writing
More postcards

9
Postcard A
1 Gill and Ruth, from Bangkok. 2 colleagues
3 Yes, they are.
Postcard B
1 Tanya's mother, from the seaside. 2 Mother and daughter.
3 Not very much.
Postcard C
1 K, from the desert. 2 (Probably) They were boyfriend and girlfriend.
3 Yes, but s/he says s/he misses Jo.

Spelling
Words with -ed and -ing

10

b	plan	planning	planned
c	disgust	disgusting	disgusted
d	surprise	surprising	surprised
e	relax	relaxing	relaxed
f	stay	staying	stayed
g	cycle	cycling	cycled
h	move	moving	moved
i	enjoy	enjoying	enjoyed
j	hope	hoping	hoped

module 7

Present Perfect
Positive, negative and question forms

1
2	Have	5	has	8	haven't	11	hasn't
3	has	6	's	9	have	12	's
4	haven't	7	hasn't	10	've		

Present Perfect and Past Simple with for

2
b	lived	e	have lived	h	has been
c	have been	f	have only known	i	has been
d	thought	g	was		

Present Perfect: short answers

3 a)
3	Yes, he has.	6	No, she hasn't.	9	Yes, they have.
4	No, he hasn't.	7	Yes, they have.		
5	No, she hasn't.	8	No, they haven't.		

Present Perfect with just, yet, already and never

4 a)
2 I've just heard that my cousin is coming to stay!!
3 I don't know. I've never tried it.
4 No, he hasn't arrived yet.
5 Not really, I've already seen it twice.

Present Perfect and Past Simple with time phrases

5
b	Have you been / haven't had	f	got married / were
c	took off	g	has been
d	've never seen	h	arrived / hasn't written
e	's been / haven't had	i	went

been or gone

6
b	been	d	gone	f	been
c	gone	e	been	g	gone

Present Perfect and Past Simple

7 a)
2	has been	7	was	12	has had
3	left	8	got	13	won
4	married	9	married	14	has returned
5	had	10	lasted	15	became
6	continued	11	has not married		

Past Participles Wordsearch

8 a)
sat – sit	run – run	lost – lose
made – make	drunk – drink	brought – bring
told – tell	got – get	seen – see
sold – sell	won – win	found – find
sung – sing	paid – pay	cost – cost
put – put	written – write	spoken – speak
chosen – choose	eaten – eat	

Vocabulary
Ambitions and dreams

9
b learn, c get, d become, e have, f play, g write, h buy

Pronunciation
The sounds /æ/ and /ʌ/

10 c)
sat /æ/	done /ʌ/	sang /æ/	become /ʌ/
come /ʌ/	drank /æ/	sung /ʌ/	ran /æ/
won /ʌ/	drunk /ʌ/	run /ʌ/	had /æ/

Improve your writing
A mini-biography

11 a)
2 B, 3 E, 4 D, 5 A, 6 C

module 8

Articles
Zero for general statements

1 a)

2 It's not true that English people drink ~~the~~ tea all the time.
3 Drinking ~~the~~ coffee helps me to wake up in the morning!
4 People in ~~the~~ Argentina often have a barbecue at the weekend.
5 ~~The~~ Japanese tea isn't the same as English tea.
6 Have you heard the news? The price of ~~the~~ petrol is going up again!
7 Marco says that the best ice cream comes from ~~the~~ Italy.
8 In ~~the~~ some parts of the United States, you can't drive until you're 18.

For general and specific statements

2

b Swiss people, The Swiss people
c books, the books
d the weather, cold weather
e the salt, Salt
f the fish, fish
g the music, music

With geographical features

3

b the, c -, d -, e -, f -, g -, h -, i the, j -, k the,
l -, m -, n the, o the, p -, q -, r the, s the, t -

Phrases with *the*: location

4

b They're in the north of Japan.
c It's on the coast of Japan.
d They're in the middle of Japan.
e They're in the south west of Japan.
f It's in the north of Japan.

Phrases with *the*: time

5

b in the evening
c in the evening
d in the morning / in the evening / at night
e in the evening
f at night
g in the afternoon
h in the evening
i in the morning
j in the morning / in the afternoon / in the evening

Other phrases with and without *the*

6

b at   e on the   h on   k on the
c by   f on the   i in the   l at
d at   g by   j at

Vocabulary
Geographical features

7

b deserts, c climate, d scenery, e the coast, f islands,
g volcanoes, h ports, i cathedrals, j canals,
k historical monuments

Vocabulary booster: things you find in cities

8 a)

2 a square
3 an art gallery
4 a bus station
5 a fountain
6 a bridge
7 a market
8 a motorway
9 a mosque
10 a park
11 a church
12 skyscrapers

c)

Buildings	Transport	Open Spaces	Other
a church	a bus station	a park	a bridge
an art gallery	a motorway	a square	a fountain
a mosque			a market
skyscrapers			a statue

Spelling
Plural nouns

9 b)

2 potatoes, 3 babies, 4 women, 5 watches, 6 men,
7 tomatoes, 8 teeth, 9 countries, 10 lives,
11 wives, 12 flies,

Listen and read

10 b)

2 55 kph
3 850
4 60%
5 on the island of Hawaii
6 79 AD
7 in the Caribbean Sea
8 May 8th 1902
9 30,000 (less two)
10 2
11 1991
12 more than 100,000

Improve your writing
Formal letters and informal notes

11 a)

He should apply for the 'Italiano in Italia' course.

b)

2 15.11.01
3 Dear Ms McGowan
4 I read
5 I am interested in
6 Please send
7 the above address
8 Yours sincerely
9 Monday
10 Hi Antonella!
11 Just a quick note to say
12 I'm sure I'll really enjoy reading it!
13 I'm sending you
14 All my love,
15 Colin

module 9

may, might, will, definitely, etc.
will / won't

1 a)

2 People won't use cash: they will only use credit cards.
3 Astronauts will visit the planet Mars.
4 Great Britain won't have a King or Queen.
5 The countries of Western Europe will all use the same currency.
6 The millennium bug will destroy the world's computers.

may / might

2

b We may / might go abroad for our holidays this year.
c They may / might not be able to finish the work until next week.
d You should take your coat; it may / might get cold later.
e Your mother may / might not want to go out this evening.
f Martha may / might not be able to help you.
g The Prime Minister may / might resign if things don't get better soon.
h I always buy a lottery ticket: I may / might win £1 million one day!

will / won't / may / might

4 a)

2 Leo, 3 Virgo, 4 Gemini, 5 Taurus

b)
Taurus
<u>You might have an argument</u> with an important person today. If this happens, <u>you'll need help. A friend or partner will be very useful to you.</u> And who knows ... <u>you might win the argument!!</u>

Gemini
<u>This will be another busy work day</u> for you: <u>you'll have all the normal things</u> to do, but <u>there may also be an extra job or two.</u> But don't worry, <u>you'll succeed!!</u> And think how <u>happy you'll be</u> when you finish!

Cancer
<u>You may have to choose</u> between your public and your private life today. <u>You won't spend much time</u> with your loved ones until later in the week. Make sure they know you love them, or <u>they may feel forgotten.</u>

Leo
<u>This will be your lucky day</u> for education! If you're still at school, <u>it'll be a good day</u> for study – something you've always thought was too hard for you <u>will be easy.</u> If you've already left school, think about going back to your studies – <u>you won't regret it!</u>

Virgo
<u>There will be some money worries</u> today. Check what you're spending – <u>you may need to spend some extra money on travel,</u> but if you buy something for a loved one, <u>they may not thank you for it!!</u>

Present tense after *if, when, before* and other time words
Present tense after *if*

5

b If you work hard, you'll pass all your exams.
c If you're late for class again, your teacher will get very annoyed.
d If you don't get up soon, you'll be late for class.
e If the train arrives on time, we'll be home before midnight.
f If you don't take a map, you'll get lost.
g If we see a restaurant, we'll stop and have lunch.

Time clauses: *if, when, before, as soon as*

6

b	If	e	if	h	as soon as
c	when	f	when	i	when
d	before	g	Before		

Word order

7

b There definitely won't be any snow tonight.
c Stefan will definitely be at home tomorrow.
d He probably won't know the answer to your question.
e We will definitely be able to give you an answer next week.

Vocabulary
Modern and traditional

8 a)

electronic goods	microwave, mobile phone, personal computer, cassette player, electronic organiser, photocopier
places to eat	fast food restaurant
places where you go shopping	mall, hypermarket, corner shop
things for cooking	cooker (microwave)
things you can play	computer game, compact disc
things you can send	e-mail, letter, fax
things you write in	address book, diary

b)
2 diary, 3 address book, 4 hypermarket, 5 photocopier

Vocabulary booster: technology

9 a)

1 answering machine, 2 keyboard, 3 laptop, 4 computer, 5 mouse mat, 6 screen, 7 fax machine, 8 mouse, 9 video recorder, 10 printer

c)

people often have at home	answering machine, video recorder
you can carry around with you	laptop
people use at work	computer, keyboard, mouse, mouse mat, screen, printer, fax machine

Pronunciation
Different pronunciations of the letter 'i'

10 b)

2	traditional	/ɪ/	8	competition	/ɪ/
3	survive	/aɪ/	9	mobile	/aɪ/
4	public transport	/ɪ/	10	equipment	/ɪ/
5	definitely	/ɪ/	11	might	/aɪ/
6	bicycle	/aɪ/	12	deliver	/ɪ/
7	library	/aɪ/			

module 10

Past Continuous
Important moments in history

1

b was reading   e were sitting   h were singing
c was playing   f were watching
d was becoming   g was waiting

Past Continuous and Past Simple

2

1 I was watching TV at home when someone came to the door.
2 My mother phoned while I was preparing dinner.
3 When we arrived home, some friends were waiting for us.
4 As I was walking along the street, I saw an old friend.
5 When I woke up, everyone was looking at me.
6 Jane saw another guest who was wearing exactly the same hat!

3

b	met	k	thought	t	was
c	was leaving	l	looked	u	arrived
d	invited	m	didn't say	v	told
e	told	n	asked	w	opened
f	made	o	explained	x	saw
g	was writing	p	was doing	y	was waiting
h	was listening	q	invited	z	fainted
i	rang	r	was making		
j	was standing	s	looked		

used to / didn't use to

4

b He used to have a moustache.
c He used to wear an old T-shirt.
d He used to have a very boring job.
e He used to work in a hamburger restaurant.
f He used to be poor.

5

b He didn't use to live in Scotland.
c He didn't use to drive a Rolls Royce.
d He didn't use to have a private plane.
e He didn't use to wear designer clothes.

Vocabulary
Accidents

6

a	fell	d	broke	g	bleeding
b	cut	e	hurt	h	bumped
c	touch	f	dropped	i	burn

Other health words

7

b	pain	e	medicine	h	rest
c	exercise	f	plaster		
d	prescription	g	doctor		

Articles

8

b a / -, c a / - / the, d -, e The / - / -, f a / a

Listen and read

9

a up to eighteen   d seven
b eight   e No
c It increases the chance of serious illness, people often die young and do less well at work.   f No

Pronunciation
Different ways of saying the letter 'c'

10 b)

exercise /s/	century /s/	crash /k/
backache /k/	children /tʃ/	school /k/
chest /tʃ/	cure /k/	accident /ks/
headache /k/	electricity /k/ /s/	

Improve your writing
Adverbs

11

b eventually   d immediately   f certainly
c Suddenly   e fortunately

module 11

Gerunds (-ing forms)
Expressing likes and dislikes

1

Typical answers might be:
Driving very fast is dangerous.
Climbing mountains is hard work.
Jogging is good for you.
Travelling by plane is good fun.
Working on a computer makes you tired.
Walking in the country helps you to relax.
Driving on the motorway is very boring.
Swimming in the sea is good fun.
Going to the gym is good for you.
Sunbathing is bad for you.
Studying English is hard work / good fun etc.

Gerunds after prepositions

2 a)

2   When I was young, I was interested in collecting stamps.
3   I'm very sorry. I'm not good at remembering people's names.
4   They left the restaurant without paying the bill.
5   Why don't you do something instead of just sitting there?
6   Are you frightened of walking alone at night?
7   Katrina's obsessed with making money.
8   My father was OK about lending me the car.
9   My sister is mad about shopping for clothes.

Verbs of liking and disliking

3

c   Joseph can't stand / absolutely loathes / really hates singing, but Jessica is keen on / likes it.
d   They both really love / both really enjoy / are both crazy about reading.
e   Joseph really loves / enjoys / is crazy about playing computer games, but Jessica doesn't really like / isn't very keen on them.
f   Joseph doesn't mind cooking, but Jessica really loves / enjoys / is crazy about it.
g   They both like / are both keen on chocolate.
h   Joseph doesn't really like / isn't very keen on doing / homework, but Jessica doesn't mind it.

Gerunds and infinitives
like doing and *would like to do*

4 a)

2   likes
3   I'd like to speak
4   Would you like to go
5   would love to go
6   she doesn't like walking
7   would love to be
8   I'd like to go

5

b	live	f	drinking	j	Getting
c	smoking	g	buying	k	spending
d	shopping	h	sleep	l	listen
e	eating	i	shaking	m	drinking

me too / so do I etc.

6 a)

2   Neither am I.
3   Yes, me too.
4   So did I.
5   Me neither.
6   Really? So am I.
7   Yes, so was I!
8   Neither did I.
9   Yes, me too.
10 Neither can I.

Vocabulary booster: -ed and -ing adjectives

7 a)

2   excited
3   interested
4   frightened
5   worried
6   tired
7   bored
8   relaxed

d)

2   relaxing
3   bored
4   surprising
5   interested
6   relaxing
7   exciting
8   worried
9   tired

Spelling
Words ending with -ion

8 a)

2   decision
3   description
4   discussion
5   education
6   explanation
7   invitation
8   permission
9   preparation
10 pronunciation

b)

1   fashion
2   ambition
3   obsession
4   conversation
5   professional
6   relationship
7   traditional
8   revision
9   nationality

Pronunciation
Words ending with -ion

9 a)

2   edu<u>ca</u>tion
3   dis<u>cus</u>sion
4   re<u>la</u>tionship
5   de<u>ci</u>sion
6   conver<u>sa</u>tion
7   per<u>mis</u>sion
8   tra<u>di</u>tional
9   oc<u>ca</u>sion
10 re<u>vi</u>sion
11 <u>fa</u>shion
12 nation<u>a</u>lity

module 12

Passive forms
Identifying Passive forms

1

b	P	e	P	h	A
c	A	f	A	i	A
d	A	g	P	j	P

Present Simple Passive

2

a	are made	d	are stolen	g	are killed
b	is used	e	are spoken	h	are lost
c	are bitten	f	is covered		

Past Simple Passive

3

b	were bought	f	was held	j	was murdered
c	was launched	g	were seen	k	was attended
d	were given	h	was known	l	was comforted
e	were filled	i	were worn		

Future Simple Passive

4

b	will be joined	f	will be made
c	will be solved	g	will be replaced
d	will be done	h	will be chosen
e	will be controlled		

Listen and read

5 b)

2 A £16.5 million diamond was sold in Geneva in 1995.
3 Diamonds are found in many countries, including South Africa and The Russian Federation.
4 Colourless diamonds are made into jewels.
5 Black diamonds are used in industry.
6 The Transvaal government gave the Cullinan diamond to King Edward VII.
7 The diamond was cut into smaller diamonds.
8 Peter Fabergé made an egg which was sold for $5.5 million at Christie's.

Active or Passive?

6

2 b, 3 a, 4 a, 5 b, 6 a, 7 b, 8 a

Relative clauses with *which*, *who* and *that*

7

b that   c who   d that   e that   f which

8

b Henry's got a hat which / that is red, green and blue.
c Claire is a writer who is very famous.
d It's a salad which / that tastes delicious.
e This is a picture which / that was painted by Monet.
f He's a teacher who is very popular.
g It's a machine which / that makes pasta.

Vocabulary

Designer goods

9

b	advertising	f	spend money on	j	own
c	save up for	g	just as good	k	looks better
d	better quality	h	costs far too	l	possessions
e	waste of money	i	can't afford		

Everyday objects

10

b	an umbrella	g	a key
c	a pair of sunglasses	h	a torch
d	a tin opener	i	a cigarette lighter
e	a comb	j	a telephone
f	an ashtray		

Spelling / Pronunciation

Silent *g* and *gh*

11 b)

b	laugh	/f/		h	enough	/f/
c	bright	silent		i	disgusting	/g/
d	bought	silent		j	signature	/g/
e	straight	silent		k	height	silent
f	frightened	silent		l	greengrocer	/g/
g	sign	silent				

Improve your writing

Joining sentences with *which*, *who*, *and*, *because* and *but*

12 a)

2 It was my grandfather who gave it to me on my 18th birthday.
3 It's made of gold and has the letters H.M. on it.
4 I always think of my family when I look at it because it used to belong to my great-grandfather.
5 I've had many presents since then but this has always been my favourite.

module 13

Present Perfect Continuous

1

b It's been raining for two hours.
c They've been playing tennis for half an hour.
d They've been walking for four hours.

Time phrases with *for* and *since*

2

c	for twenty minutes	i	since this morning
d	since he was born	j	since you left school
e	since Thursday	k	for six months
f	since then	l	for an hour
g	since last week	m	for twenty years
h	since 9 o'clock		

Present Perfect with *for* and *since*

3

b	since then	f	since 1990
c	since you left school	g	for an hour
d	since this morning	h	for twenty years
e	since he was born		

4

b He has been working at the National Theatre for a year.
c He has been working on *Romeo and Juliet* for two weeks.
d She has been living in England for four years.
e She has been working at *La Finca* for two years.
f *La Finca II* has been operating for a week.
g She has been living in England for almost twenty years.
h She has been studying yoga for about ten years.
i She has been teaching yoga for a year and a half.

Present Perfect Simple or Continuous with stative verbs

5

e I've liked chocolate for years.
f Have you known Sylvia for a long time?
h I haven't seen Michael for years and years.

Vocabulary
Jobs and Personal Characteristics

6

b well-qualified   h sympathetic
c patient   i imagination
d experience   j honest
e smart   k well-mannered
f latest methods   l good with people
g good with money

Vocabulary booster: jobs

7

a pharmacist   f taxi driver
b tour guide   g flight attendant
c nurse   h waiter
d shop assistant   i lorry driver
e police officer   j musician

Reading

8

	1	2	3	4
the job	management trainee	Waitress	Ground crew	Chef
where is it	Samui Island, Thailand	Island of Sark, Channel Islands	Europe: France, Italy, Austria, Switzerland	Tallinn, Estonia
dates	July – September 2001	end May – mid-September	24 May – 30 October	6 months
you need to ...	speak fluent English	experience not essential	be fit with a cheerful personality	qualified chef
salary	6,000 baht per month	–	small salary	$800-$1000

Pronunciation
Some 'hard to pronounce' words

9

honest - not   awful - more
patient - painting   health - fell
psychiatrist - fire   architect - headache

Improve your writing
Error correction

10

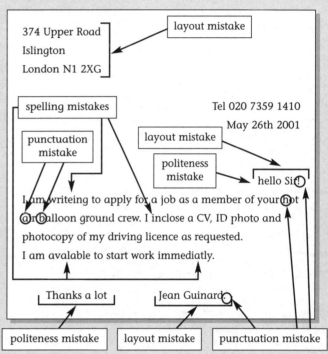

The correct version is:

374 Upper Road
Islington
London N1 2XG

Tel. 020 7359 1410

May 26th 2001

Dear Sir
    I am writing to apply for a job as a member of your Hot Air Balloon ground crew. I enclose a CV, ID photo and photocopy of my driving licence as requested. I am available to start work immediately.

Yours faithfully
Jean Guinard

module 14

some, *any* and quantifiers
some, *any* and *no*

1

b	some	d	any	f	no / some	h	any
c	some	e	no	g	some	i	no

much, *many*, *a lot of*, *a few*, *no*

2

2	many	4	a lot of	6	no	8	no
3	a lot of	5	a few	7	a / a lot of		

too and *not ... enough*

3

b was too cold / wasn't warm enough
c isn't big enough / is too small
d wasn't fast enough / was too slow
e was too high / wasn't low enough
f 's too small / isn't tall enough

Prepositions
Describing where things are

4

There's an egg behind the candle.
There's an egg between the fireplace and the bookcase.
There's an egg in front of the fireplace.
There's an egg on top of the bookcase.
There's an egg on top of the fireplace./next to the elephant.
There's an egg opposite the bookcase.
There's an egg at the bottom of the staircase.
There's an egg under the chair.
There's an egg in the corner (stuck on the wall).
There's an egg near the chair.
There's an egg inside the vase.
There's an egg outside the window.
There's an egg inside the fireplace.
There's an egg behind the mirror.

Vocabulary
Adjectives for describing places

5

b	A	private	large	~~wooden~~	sunny	**garden.**
c	A(n)	modern	spacious	attractive	~~private~~	**kitchen.**
d	A(n)	old-fashioned	~~private~~	wooden	elegant	**table.**
e	A(n)	colourful	elegant	simple	~~quiet~~	**dress.**
f	A	~~dark~~	simple	large	lovely	**meal.**
g	A(n)	~~three-storey~~	old-fashioned	dark	attractive	**room.**

Prepositions

6

b	on	d	at	f	in	h	in
c	on	e	in	g	on		

Describing houses and apartments

7

b	balcony	f	fireplace	j	path
c	buildings	g	floor	k	rug
d	courtyard	h	kitchen	l	suburbs
e	furniture	i	living room	m	village

Vocabulary booster: things in a house

8

2	l	7	g	12	p	17	j
3	d	8	b	13	i	18	r
4	e	9	k	14	h		
5	c	10	o	15	m		
6	a	11	n	16	q		

Improve your writing
Notes giving directions

10

b When you come out of the station, turn left.
c Walk along Station Road for about fifty metres.
d There's a bus stop on your right. Take a number 11 bus to Sandy Bay.
e Get off when you see a large petrol station on the corner. It takes about ten minutes.
f Cross the road and walk about 100 metres.
g Take the first turning on your left, where you see a sign saying 'Holiday Apartments'.
h Go down the hill towards the sea – you'll see the 'Holiday Apartments' office on your right. It's open from 9 to 5.

Spelling
Same pronunciation, different spelling (homophones)

11

2	here	5	road	8	there
3	ate	6	past	9	by
4	right	7	see	10	eight

module 15

Past Perfect

1

2	had paid	6	had won
3	hadn't slept	7	hadn't flown
4	hadn't seen	8	had left
5	had broken down		

Past Perfect and Past Simple

2

b	was	h	didn't know
c	had arrested	i	had bought
d	found	j	had sold
e	wasn't	k	had
f	had tried	l	died
g	had emigrated		

Reported speech
Direct to reported speech

3

b   He said (that) the house had belonged to his grandfather.
c   He said (that) his grandfather had died the previous month.
d   He said (that) he didn't want to sell the house, but he couldn't afford to keep it.
e   He said (that) Mr Taylor and his family would be very happy there.
f   He said (that) the house was worth $100,000, but he'd sell it to him for $50,000.

Reported to direct speech

4

b   'I live with my mother at 43 Fountain Road, Denton.'
c   'I spent the evening watching *The Lion King* at the ABC Cinema.'
d   'I fell asleep during the film, so I can't remember the story.'
e   'The film finished at about 10.30.'
f   'After the film, I took a Number 85 bus home to Fountain Road.'
g   'I went to bed at 12 o'clock, after my mum read me a story.'

Prepositions

5

b	in	d	into	f	by
c	on	e	in	g	by

Irregular Past forms

6

b	sang	d	stole	f	broken
c	driven	e	written	g	seen

Vocabulary
Verb phrases to do with money

7

2	lent / Phil	5	wasted	8	bet
3	earn	6	win	9	invest
4	owe	7	save	10	lost

Listen and read

8 a)

2   pieces of paper
3   a £10 bank note
4   about 2,700 years ago
5   began to appear
6   But they weren't used in Europe
7   as people became rich
8   a thing of the past

c)
1   Only in theory.
2   No – the government stopped exchanging them in 1971.
3   a) precious shells   b) jewellery   c) blocks of dried tea
4   People in ancient Lydia (Turkey). About 2,700 years ago.
5   In the 11th century. In China.
6   In the Middle Ages.
7   'smart cards'.

Pronunciation
The sounds /eɪ/ and /e/

9 b)

2   They wasted all the money we gave them.
    /eɪ/   /eɪ/   /e/
3   You said you'd never played tennis until today!
    /e/   /e/ /eɪ/ /e/   /eɪ/
4   Have you read the book I lent you, by the way?
         /e/   /e/   /eɪ/
5   She said she'd pay me back at the end of April.
    /e/   /eɪ/   /e/
6   Jane made a terrible mistake.
    /eɪ/ /eɪ/   /e/   /eɪ/

say or *tell*

10

b	told	e	said	h	Tell
c	said	f	say		
d	tell	g	told		

Improve your writing
Punctuation in direct speech

11

2   'I didn't play very well today,' Peter Salmon said, 'but I still think I can win tomorrow.'
3   'Where are you going?' the policeofficer asked us.
4   'Two coffees, please,' I said to the waiter, 'and can we have the bill, please?'
5   'Are you ready yet?' shouted Neil's mother. 'I'm waiting.'
6   'I've bought you a present,' said Christine, 'I hope you like it.'

module 16

would and *wouldn't*

1

b	wouldn't	d	wouldn't	f	would
c	would	e	wouldn't	g	wouldn't

Second Conditional

2

b	didn't work / wouldn't have	f	had / would take
c	would feel / didn't get up	g	spoke / would be
d	could / would you like	h	had / would get
e	would do / weren't		

might or *would* in Second Conditional sentences

3

2   She wouldn't go out with him if he didn't have so much money.
3   If I could go on holiday anywhere in the world, I'd go to Florida.
4   Robert might do better at school if he did his homework regularly.
5   If you told her the truth, she might get very angry.
6   If you didn't drink so much coffee before going to bed, you might sleep better.

First and Second Conditional forms

4

2	a	4	b	6	b
3	a	5	a	7	a

will or would?

5

b	I'll	e	wouldn't	h	would
c	I'd	f	I'll	i	she'd
d	will	g	I'll		

Short answers with will and would

6

b	No, he won't.	f	No, I wouldn't.
c	No, I wouldn't.	g	Yes, I do. / Yes, they will.
d	Yes, we will.	h	No, I wouldn't.
e	Yes, I would.		

Vocabulary

Wordbuilding

7

b	tragically	e	violent
c	peaceful	f	freely
d	strong		

Vocabulary booster: people in politics, religion and public life

8 a)

1 **with a particular religion**

a Muslim   a Buddhist
a Protestant   a Hindu
a Christian

2 **with a religious 'job'**

a priest

3 **with particular political ideas**

a communist
a social democrat
a green

4 **in politics**

a mayor   the President
a government minister   a Member of Parliament
the Prime Minister   the Vice President

5 **who is royal**

a King
a Queen

6 **who works with the law**

a judge

d)

1	Muslims	5	a Queen
2	communist	6	government minister
3	Catholic	7	Hindus
4	Prime Minister	8	the President

Spelling

Silent 'w'

9 b)

wrong   answer   whose
whole   songwriter   wrote

c)

1 wrong / wrote
2 whole / whose
3 answer

Improve your writing

Error correction

11 b)

1	writing	12	name's
2	unfortunately	13	René
3	it's	14	that's
4	different	15	who
5	England	16	English
6	and	17	sitting
7	boring	18	said
8	which / that	19	?
9	so	20	'Fine, thanks,'
10	doctor	21	getting
11	France	22	friends

Articles

Zero for general statements

1 a) Find and cross out the unnecessary *the* in each sentence below.

1 ~~The~~ Coca-Cola is one of the most popular drinks in the world.

2 It's not true that English people drink the tea all the time.

3 Drinking the coffee helps me to wake up in the morning!

4 People in the Argentina often have a barbecue at the weekend.

5 The Japanese tea isn't the same as English tea.

6 Have you heard the news? The price of the petrol is going up again!

7 Marco says that the best ice cream comes from the Italy.

8 In the some parts of the United States, you can't drive until you're 18.

b) 📼 Listen to the sentences on the tape. Practise saying them.

For general and specific statements

2 Look at the pairs of sentences and <u>underline</u> the correct phrase.

> **LOOK!**
>
> We do not use *the* when we talk about things or people **in general**.
>
> *Dogs make very good pets.*
>
> We use *the* to talk about **specific** things or people.
> *The people in my street are very friendly.*
> *'Where's the milk?' 'It's in the fridge'*

a 'Where's *coffee* / <u>*the coffee*</u>?' 'It's in the cupboard on the left.'
   I always drink <u>*coffee*</u> / *the coffee* at breakfast time.

b *Swiss people* / *The Swiss people* all learn two languages at school.
   The Swiss people / *Swiss people* in my class all speak German.

c These days, it's easy to buy *books* / *the books* over the Internet.
   Where are *books* / *the books* you borrowed from the library?

d What's *the weather* / *weather* like today?
   Some people think that people work harder in *cold weather* / *the cold weather*.

e Can you pass me *salt* / *the salt* please?
   Salt / *The salt* is bad for you if you eat too much of it.

f This river is so polluted that all *fish* / *the fish* have died.
   Eating *fish* / *the fish* is very good for your heart.

g I went to see *Chicago* last night: *music* / *the music* was great!
   I sometimes listen to *the music* / *music* when I'm working.

With geographical features

3 Read the Fact File about Japan. Complete the text using *the* or – .

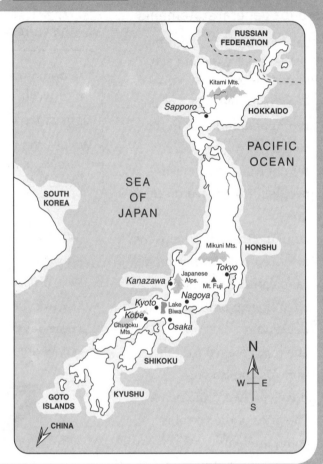

Japan: Fact file

(a)..–........... Japan is not one island, but a group of over a thousand islands in (b).............. Pacific Ocean, in the east of (c).............. Asia. The four largest islands are (d).............. Hokkaido, (e).............. Honshu, (f).............. Kyushu, and (g).............. Shikoku. Japan's nearest neighbours are (h).............. North and South Korea across (i).............. Sea of Japan, (j).............. China and (k).............. Russian Federation. There are a number of volcanic mountains, including (l).............. Mount Fuji and (m).............. Mount Aso. Other important mountain ranges are (n).............. Chukogu Mountains and (o).............. Japanese Alps not far from (p).............. Nagoya, the third city. Hokkaido is the furthest north of the main islands. The main city is (q).............. Sapporo on (r).............. River Ishikari. Popular holiday places are (s).............. Kitami Mountains and (t).............. Lake Kussharo.

Phrases with *the*: location

4 Look again at the map of Japan and answer the questions using the word in brackets.

a Which part of Japan is Tokyo in? (*east*)
It's in the east of Japan.

b Where are the Kitami Mountains? (*north*)
....

c Where is Kanazawa? (*coast*)
....

d Where are the Mikuni Mountains? (*middle*)
....

e Where are the Goto Islands? (*south west*)
....

f Where is the island of Hokkaido? (*north*)
....

Phrases with *the*: time

5 When do people usually do these things? Answer with *in the morning,* etc.

a have breakfast   *in the morning*

b watch TV   ....

c have dinner   ....

d feel tired   ....

e go dancing   ....

f dream   ....

g come home from school / work ....

h meet friends   ....

i get up   ....

j have a coffee   ....